The History of the Radio Officer
in the British Merchant Navy
and on Deep-Sea Trawlers

1. Marchese Marconi, G.C.V.O., LL.D., D.Sc.

The History of the Radio Officer in the British Merchant Navy and on Deep-Sea Trawlers

by

JOANNA GREENLAW

Published by

CYHOEDDWYR
DINEFWR
PUBLISHERS

in conjunction with Joanna Greenlaw

Published by
Dinefwr Publishers
Rawlings Road, Llandybie, Carmarthenshire
Wales, SA18 3YD
Telephone Sales: (01269) 851989
E-mail: dinefwr.press@btopenworld.com
in conjuction with
Joanna Greenlaw. Telephone: (01792) 425494

A CIP catalogue record for this book is
available from the British Library.

ISBN 1 904323 01 4

Printed and bound in Wales by
Dinefwr Press Ltd.
Rawlings Road, Llandybie
Carmarthenshire, SA18 3YD

Front colour photograph:
By kind permission of the Board of Trustees of the
National Museums and Galleries on Merseyside.

This book is dedicated to the comrades of my youth, whom I now see very clearly, but from great distance. And what I chiefly remember are not the U-boats and the sinkings, but the laughter and the hoary old jokes we had all heard before, nights ashore in far-flung places, and crowding together in someone's cabin with a case of twenty-four cans of Barclays beer on the deck between us and the air thick with cigarette smoke.

And my salutation goes out to them across the hills of time.

Contents

Foreword

WINDSOR CASTLE

The author has a very remarkable story to tell. There cannot have been many - if any - other women who went to sea as Radio Officers in the Merchant Navy during the Second World War. Even fewer might have reached the upper reaches of management of the Marconi International Marine Communications Co. Ltd. twenty years later.

This is both a fascinating personal story and a comprehensive history of professional Radio Officers in the Merchant Navy and it is told by an experienced historian. Since Radio Officers no longer exist, this book is the definitive account of a profession that provided a vital service to the Merchant Navy during a very important period of its modern development.

Philip

Introduction

FIVE YEARS AGO, after completing a long and arduous writing task, I wrote in the preface of the book that followed: 'In asking myself why, in my seventies, I embarked on the daunting amount of research, travel, expense, and sheer slog that a work of this kind demands, my answer has to be that of Sir Richard Burton, Victorian explorer, soldier, poet, translator, geologist, swordsman, author and raconteur – "Damned fool! The Devil drives!"'

Five years later, after completing another literary marathon, the same question produces a similar reply; the condition, it would seem, is not improving.

The idea of writing this book came to me quite suddenly in May 2001, while I was having lunch in the main square of the little hill village of St-Guilhem-le-Désert near Béziers in south-west France. By then I had written four books – three non-fiction and one novel – all successful. Yet the subject of this one, so relevant to my own life, had not occurred to me. I realise now, that for all sorts of reasons, the time had not been ripe. Then suddenly I understood that this was a task which had to be completed before I could concentrate on anything else.

The fact is that I was peculiarly suited to write it. I went to sea as a Radio Officer in the Merchant Navy in 1942 with a spark transmitter and a two valve receiver – it was an old ship, built in the mid-20s. I now believe that there is a mysterious force which governs our life and sets a period upon it. Some call it Fate, and in the East, where I have spent important periods of my life, it is called Kismet. And through its mysterious workings, by 1963 I had become the Personnel and Operations Manager of the Marconi International Marine Communication Company in Chelmsford, Essex, in charge of a sea staff of more than 2,500 Radio Officers, 400 on Deep-Sea Trawlers, Traffic Operation and Accounting, Training, and the supporting shore technical staff at home and abroad which formed the company's world-wide servicing network.

Here I must stress that, as the book's title implies, it is not a history of the Marconi Company, although until the early 1920s the history of wireless at sea was inseparable from Marconi and his company. But after that came many other manufacturers of wireless equipment and employers of Radio Officers.

In the early 1970s private considerations caused me to throw the whole lot up, and I returned to sea as a Radio Officer until 1984. This included eight months in the Falklands during 1982/83 as Chief Radio Officer of the ex-Sealink Ferry *St Edmund*, hurriedly withdrawn from service to convey the Royal Hampshires and three regiments of Gurkhas to confront General Galtieri's forces in Port Stanley.

The Merchant Radio Officer, known to generations of seafarers as 'Sparks' was as integral a part of life on board as the engine room or funnel. He, (and later she) provided the link between the ship and the shore, the channels for orders, weather reports and private messages. And, when disaster threatened, was often the only means of attracting help. If the tradition of the sea meant that the Captain was the last to leave his ship, then the Radio Officer was usually the last but one.

The nickname 'Sparks' was inevitable from the time when the first practitioner of the mysterious art of wireless communication at sea thumped away at a Morse key, producing the raspy note and hiss of electrical energy as blue sparks and the smell of ozone radiated from the silver plated spark gap which constituted the heart of his occult contraption.

Today, the advent of satellite communication, teleprinters and facsimile has rendered the traditional Radio Officer, whose art was based on the Morse Code, as extinct an animal as the Brontosaurus. He has passed into marine history like the lamp-trimmer on a sailing ship or the donkey-man on a steam tramp, taking with him his world of dots and dashes, SOS messages and telegram forms.

And it is only right that the first chapter of this book begins with the first Radio Officer of all, Guglielmo Marconi.

CHAPTER 1

Guglielmo Marconi – The First Radio Officer

THERE IS A FAMOUS PHOTOGRAPH of Guglielmo Marconi taken in London in 1896 which shows a serious young man of twenty-two years seated at a table in front of the mysterious paraphernalia which comprised his invention. On his left is a square wooden box with an ordinary Morse Code sounder on top of it. It is connected by a copper strip to a wooden framework supporting two coils of electrical windings with brass rods on either side, each terminated by a brass sphere. He appears incredibly neat and tidy; not a hair is out of place, and he stares out at us over a winged collar with a curiously thoughtful and even challenging expression. His right hand supports his chin and he has the big sticking-out ears which phrenologists have traditionally associated with a powerful and dominating personality.

Marconi is usually referred to as 'the man who invented wireless telegraphy' – though the Russian adherents of a certain Mr Popoff warmly dispute his claim – but in fact he was not. Marconi's genius was to bring together in a practical form discoveries already made, and translate them into a successful means of wireless communication.

In 1878 William Henry Preece (1834-1913) was appointed Assistant Engineer in Chief of the British Post Office, becoming Chief Engineer in 1892 and a KCB in 1899.

Around 1882 Preece and others discovered that electrical signals conveyed by a telegraph wire created interference in adjacent wires. Moreover, if the wires were parallel, the effect was greatly increased and the interaction of the varying magnetic field around the first would produce a corresponding signal in the latter. In the mid-1880s Heinrich Hertz, Professor of Theoretical Physics at the University of Kiel, demonstrated that the changing electro-magnetic field in turn created electro-magnetic waves in space which obeyed the laws of optics and travelled at the speed of light.

By using an induction coil to produce high voltages, the range of the

2. Marconi as a child, with his mother and elder brother, Alfonso.
(Photograph: Marconi plc)

field could be greatly increased. What had yet to be discovered was an efficient means of detecting the signals by some kind of receiving device.

However, and again coincidentally, in the late 1880s Edouard Branly, Professor of Physics at the Catholic University of Paris, found that if a quantity of suitable metal filings were contained within a glass tube between two electrodes, their electrical resistance altered if the tube was subjected to a varying electro-magnetic wave.

In 1894 at a meeting of the Royal Institution, Professor Sir Oliver Lodge showed that the 'Branly Tube', as he christened it, acted as a coherer, i.e. the filings became cohered – packed together – which reduced their electrical resistance if subjected to an electro-magnetic wave. When the wave was no longer present the filings returned to their original state of high resistance (de-cohered), and if the tube was lightly tapped, the process was accelerated.

These separate discoveries were combined together in a practical form in the arcane paraphernalia contained within young Mr Marconi's famous black box.

The originator of wireless communication came from a well-to-do Italian landowning family, the second son of Guiseppe Marconi and Annie Jameson, who was a member of the Irish whisky-brewing family. They were married in April 1864, Annie being twenty-one and Guiseppe a widower of thirty-eight. The Marconi family had long been settled in the Appenines and the couple made their home in Guiseppe's town house in Bologna. Their first son, Alfonso, was born in 1865, and their second, Guglielmo, on 25th April 1874.

Guiseppe Marconi had inherited a country estate near Bologna, and it was here at the Villa Grifone that Guglielmo was largely brought up. At the age of thirteen he entered the Technical Institute in Livorno, where he became interested in physics and electricity. He failed the examination for the University of Bologna but this did not prevent his enthusiasm for conducting experiments into Hertzian waves. It was at the Villa Grifone that he set up a laboratory in the attic and carried out most of his early experiments.

3. Villa Grifone, Pontecchio, Bologna, Italy – the country home of the Marconi family and scene of Marconi's first experiments.
(Photograph: Marconi plc)

4. Post Office engineers examining Marconi's apparatus
during the Bristol Channel tests, 1897.
(Photograph: Marconi plc)

Using an induction coil to create a spark which energised a Hertz Radiator, and a Branly coherer as a receiver, he gradually increased the distance from across a room, down the corridor, and then from the house into the fields.

His great leap forward was to replace the Hertzian electrodes by two copper plates, one at the top of a long pole and the other at ground level. He then increased the range still further by using a vertical kite aerial and utilising the earth itself as the bottom electrode. Marconi applied for the world's first patent for wireless telegraphy on 2nd June 1896, the complete specification being approved on 2nd March 1897.

On 20th July 1897, The Wireless Telegraph and Signal Company was formed, which in February 1900 changed its name to Marconi's Wireless Telegraph Company Ltd., acquiring the rights to Marconi's patent in the process.

On 16th March 1905, Marconi married Beatrice O'Brien, whose father was Baron Inchiquin, an Irish Peer. Their first child died before it could be

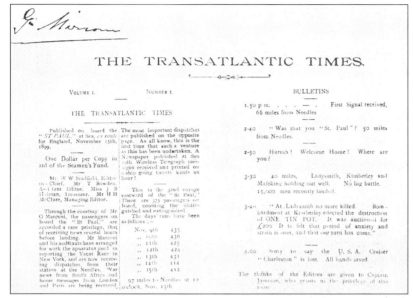

5. The first ocean newspaper, autographed by Marconi on
the date of publication, 15th November 1899.
(Photograph: Marconi plc)

christened, but three more followed: Degna, born September 1908, Guilio
in May 1910, and Gioa in April 1916. The marriage proved to be an unhappy
one, and it was annulled in February 1924. On 15th June 1927, he married
the Countess Maria Cristina Bezzi-Scali by whom he had a daughter born
20th July 1930, christened Maria Elettra Elena Anna by Cardinal Pacelli.

She was the daughter of Count Francesco Bezzi Scali, who was Brigadier
General of the Papal Guard. Maria's family connection with the Vatican was
of great help to Marconi, and probably played a part in Pope Pius XI's
request for him to set up the Vatican Radio Broadcasting Station, which was
inaugurated on 12th February 1931. At this ceremony the Pope addressed the
world, ending his speech with the words 'Urbi et Orbi'. And in February
1933 Marconi set up a micro-wave link between Vatican City and the Papal
summer residence at Castel Gandolfo.

He developed serious heart trouble in 1927 and his condition gradually
deteriorated. Three days after an audience with the Pope on 17th July
1937, Marconi died of a heart attack at the age of sixty-four. He was given a
state funeral in Rome and, as a mark of respect, at the hour of his funeral a
radio silence descended over most of the world. In the British Isles all Post
Office wireless telegraph stations were silent for two minutes. Silence was
also observed at all broadcasting stations controlled by the BBC.

Marconi was remembered by those who knew him as a man of few words; orderly, precise, and methodical, and though he gave an impression of remoteness to strangers, within the circle of his own friends he was excellent company.

There is a nice story of Marconi when he visited the Chicago World Fair in 1933. Discovering that there was an amateur radio station at the fair, he paid it a surprise visit. After inspecting the equipment very closely he remarked that it was a very fine piece of work. When the proud recipients of his praise protested that they were only amateurs, he replied: 'Ah! But I am only an amateur myself.'

Not many people knew that he lost his right eye after a car accident in Spezia in 1913, and his great friend the Marchese Solari observed that Marconi possessed exceptional resistance to pain as a result of an indomitable will power. He now lies buried in the crypt at the Villa Grifone alongside his second wife, Maria Cristina.

In 1938 the Fondazione Guglielmo Marconi was established at the Villa Grifone, which is now a museum associated with the University of Bologna and a point of world reference for research into the history of radio-communication. Throughout his life he received many international honours and awards. Among the most notable was the joint award of the Nobel Prize for Physics, the Albert Medal of the Royal Society of Arts, the Kelvin Medal, election to the Presidency of the Italian Royal Academy, and the Italian National Scientific Research Council. He was made a citizen of Rome, Senator Marchese, Knight of the Order of St Anne, and Knight Grand Cross of the Royal Victorian Order.

WIRELESS AT SEA – THE BEGINNINGS

The first wireless telegraph experiments over water were carried out by Marconi in May 1897 from a transmitter set up at Lavernock Point near Penarth in South Wales. Communication was established with a receiver situated three and a half miles away on the island of Flat Holm in the Bristol Channel, and also to Brean Down in Somerset, a distance of nine miles.

This historic event was commemorated on 12th May 1948, when a bronze plaque was erected by the Cardiff Rotary Club on the wall of St Lawrence Church, close to where the original experiments were carried out.

Over September/October 1899 the famous contest took place between the *Shamrock* and the *Columbia* in the International Yacht Race in the waters

'. . . it was some fifty years ago we were sitting together—just as you and I might be—when I said, "Marconi," I said, "Why don't you invent wireless?" "Good idea, Bob," he said, "*I'll* invent wireless and *you'll* go to sea and operate it for me." '

6. *(Cartoon courtesy of Marconi plc & Norman Mansbridge)*

off New York. Marconi was present in New York at the time and supervised the reporting of the races as they occurred from a suitably equipped ship to a shore station where in less than five hours messages of more than four thousand words were transmitted by land telegraph line and published by the *New York Herald*.

Marconi himself must be fully entitled to be described as the First Radio Officer at sea, because during his return journey to the UK on board the American Line s.s. *St Paul* it was he who installed his equipment on board and on 15th November 1899, established communication with the Needles Station on the Isle of White at a distance of more than sixty miles.

This epoch making event was the subject of a letter from a gentleman with the impressive name of Major Flood Page, later the Managing Director of Marconi's Wireless Telegraph Company Ltd., which appeared in *The Times* on 15th November 1899. It is worthwhile quoting the full account as follows.

As Mr Marconi left New York, he cabled to the office of the Company in London that he would speak to the Needles from the *St Paul* on their arrival in English waters. Having ascertained that the *St Paul* was

19

7. Marconi, en route across Atlantic, c.1901.

(Photograph: Marconi plc)

expected at Southampton on Wednesday, Mr Jameson Davis and I met at Yarmouth, Isle of Wight, on Tuesday afternoon and arrived at the Needles about 5 p.m. We had an assistant with us and set to work at once to speak to the Haven. Even in those days the arrival of the Atlantic steamers could not be timed to an hour, but those who we consulted seemed to agree that the *St Paul* would pass up about ten to eleven o'clock on Wednesday morning. To make assurance doubly sure one of the assistants passed the night in the instrument room, but his night was not disturbed by the ringing of his bell, and we were all left to sleep in peace. Between 6 and 7 a.m. I was down; everything was in order. The Needles resembled pillars of salt as one after the other they were lighted up by the brilliant sunrise. There was a thick haze over the sea, and it would not have been possible for the liner to pass the Needles without our catching a sight of her. We chatted away pleasantly with the Haven. Breakfast over, the sun was delicious as we paced on the lawn, but at sea the haze increased to fog; no ordinary signals could have been read from any ship passing the place at which we stood.

The idea of failure never entered into our minds. So far as we were concerned, we were ready and we felt complete confidence that the ship would be all right with Mr Marconi himself on board. Yet, as may easily be imagined, we felt in a state of nervous tension. Waiting is ever tedious, but to wait for hours for the first liner that has ever approached these or any other shores with Marconi apparatus on board, and to wait from ten to eleven, when the steamer was expected, on to twelve, to one, to two – it was not anxiety, it was certainly not doubt, not lack of confidence, but it was waiting.

We sent out our signals over and over again, when, in the most natural and ordinary way, our bell rang. It was 4.45 p.m.

'Is that you, *St Paul*?'

'Yes'

'Where are you?'

'Sixty-six nautical miles away.'

Need I confess that delight, joy, satisfaction, swept away all nervous tension, and in a few minutes we were transcribing, as if it were our daily occupation, four cablegrams for New York, and many telegrams for many parts of England and France, which had been sent fifty, forty-five, forty miles by 'wireless' to be dispatched from the Totland Bay Post Office.

The *St Paul* also has another claim to fame – it was aboard her that the first ship newspaper ever to receive news by wireless was published. The ship was still fifty miles from the Needles when the latest news of the Boer War was received and printed:

> 3.30 Ladysmith, Kimberley and Mafeking holding out well. No big battle. 15,000 men recently landed.
>
> 3.41 At Ladysmith no more killed. Bombardment at Kimberley effected the destruction of ONE TIN POT. It was auctioned for £200. It is felt that period of anxiety and strain is over, and that out turn has come.

Marconi's next challenge was to bridge the Atlantic, and in October 1900 work began on a suitable site at Poldhu, near Mullion in Cornwall. The transmitter was powered by a twenty-five kilowatt alternator producing 2,000 volts at fifty cycles which was stepped up by a suitable transformer to 20,000 volts and fed to two spark gaps in turn and suitable aerial tuning circuits. The aerial was in the form of a huge inverted cone made up of four hundred wires, sixty meters high, and supported by a circle of twenty masts. The construction work was nearly completed by March 1901 and Marconi then travelled to New York taking with him R. H. Vyvyan, his chief assistant at Poldhu, in order to set up a receiving station at Cape Cod. Having got things started he then returned to Poldhu leaving Vyvyan to complete the installation.

On 17th September 1901, all the masts collapsed during a storm, and in November the same thing happened at Cape Cod. Having lost both large aerials, Marconi decided to erect a temporary aerial at Poldhu and go to North America to at least carry out listening tests. The nearest point on the North American mainland was Newfoundland and a site was chosen at Signal Hill, near St John's, not far from where the first transatlantic telegraph cables had been brought ashore thirty-five years previously. The outcome, which occurred on 9th December 1901, is described in Marconi's own account of that historic occasion, which deserves to be reproduced in full:

> On November 26, 1901, I sailed from Liverpool on the liner *Sardinian* accompanied by two assistants, Messrs Kemp and Paget. As it was clearly impossible at that time of the year, owing to the inclement weather and especially in view of the shortness of time at our disposal

to erect high poles to support the aerial, I had arranged to have the necessary aerial supported in the air by a small captive balloon, and so we took with us two balloons as well as six kites.

8. Marconi's aerial system at Poldhu before and after the gale of 17th September 1901.
(Photograph: Marconi plc)

We landed at St John's on Friday, December 6, and the following day, before beginning operations, I visited the Governor, Sir Cavendish Boyle, the Premier, Sir Robert Bond, and other members of the Ministry, who promised me their heartiest co-operation and placed the resources of every department of the Government at my disposal in order to facilitate my work. They also offered me the temporary

9. Struggling with the kite, St John's, Newfoundland, 1901 (Marconi on the left).
(Photograph: Marconi plc)

10. Marconi seated inside the station of St John's, Signal Hill, Newfoundland, after receiving the first transatlantic signal.
(Photograph: Marconi plc)

use of such lands as I might require for the erection of depots at Cape Race, or elsewhere, if I should eventually determine to erect the wireless stations which they understood were being contemplated.

After taking a look at the various sites which might prove suitable, I considered that the best one to be found was on Signal Hill, a lofty eminence overlooking the port and forming a natural bulwark which protects it from the fury of the Atlantic gales. On top of this hill is a small plateau of some two acres in area which I thought very suitable for the manipulation of either the balloons or the kites. On a crag on this plateau rose the new Cabot Memorial Tower which was designed as a signal station, and close to it there was an old military barracks which was then used as a hospital. It was in a room in this building that I set up my apparatus and made preparations for the great experiment.

On Monday, December 9, barely three days after my arrival, I began work on Signal Hill together with my assistants. I decided to try one of the balloons first as a means of elevating the aerial and by Wednesday we had inflated it and it made its first ascent during the morning. Its diameter was about fourteen feet and it contained some 1,000 cubic feet of hydrogen gas, quite sufficient to hold up the aerial which consisted of a wire weighing about ten pounds. Owing, however, to the heavy wind that was blowing at the time, after a short while the balloon broke away and disappeared to parts unknown. I came to the conclusion that perhaps the kites would answer better, and on Thursday morning, in spite of the furious gale that was blowing, we managed to elevate one of the kites to a height of about four hundred feet.

It was a bluff, raw day; at the base of the cliff, three hundred feet below us, thundered a cold sea. Oceanward, through the mist I could discern dimly the outlines of Cape Spear, the easternmost reach of the North American Continent, while beyond that rolled the unbroken ocean, nearly two thousand miles of which stretched between me and the British coast. Across the harbour the city of St John's lay on its hillside, wrapped in fog.

The critical moment had come for which the way had been prepared by six years of hard and unremitting work in the face of all kinds of criticisms and of numerous attempts to discourage me and turn me aside from my ultimate purpose. I was about to test the truth of my theories, to prove that the three hundred patents that Marconi companies and myself had taken and the tens of thousands of pounds

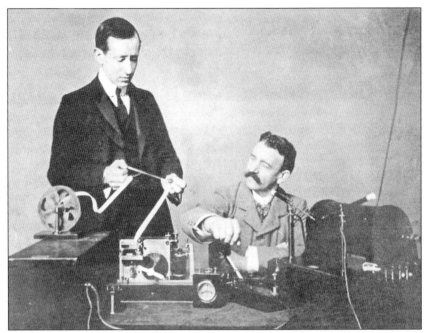

11. Marconi and George Kemp with high voltage induction coil,
coherer receiver and Morse inker, 1901.
(Photograph: Marconi plc)

which had been spent in experimenting and in the construction of
the great station at Poldhu, had not been in vain.

In view of the importance of all that was at stake I decided not to
trust to the usual arrangement of having the coherer signals recorded
automatically through a relay and a Morse instrument on paper tape,
but to use instead a telephone connected to a self-acting coherer, the
human ear being more sensitive than the recorder. Suddenly, about
half past twelve, there sounded the sharp click of the 'tapper' as it
struck the coherer, showing me that something was coming and I
listened intently.

Unmistakably, the three sharp little clicks corresponding to three
dots, sounded several times in my ear; but I would not be satisfied
without corroboration. 'Can you hear anything, Mr Kemp?' I said,
handing the telephone to my assistant. Kemp heard the same thing
as I, and I knew then that I had been right in my calculations. The
electric waves which were being sent out from Poldhu had traversed
the Atlantic, serenely ignoring the curvature of the earth which so
many doubters considered would be a fatal obstacle, and they were

now affecting my receiver in Newfoundland. I knew that the day on which I should be able to send full messages without wires or cables across the Atlantic was not far distant and, as Dr Pupin, the celebrated Serbo-American electrician, very rightly said shortly afterwards, the faintness of the signals had nothing to do with it. The distance had been overcome and further development of the sending and receiving apparatus was all that was required.

After a short while the signals stopped, evidently owing to changes in the capacity of the aerial wire which in turn were due to the varying height of the kite. But again at 1.10 and at 1.20 the three little clicks were distinctly and unmistakably heard, about twenty-five times altogether. On the following day the signals were heard again though not quite so distinctly. On Saturday a further attempt was made to obtain a repetition of the signals but owing to difficulties with the kite we had to give up the attempt. However, there was no further doubt possible that the experiment had succeeded, and that afternoon, December 14, I sent a cablegram to Major Flood Page, one of the directors of the Marconi Company, informing him that the signals had been received but that the weather had made the tests extremely difficult. That same night I also gave the news to the Press at St John's whence it was telegraphed to all parts of the world.

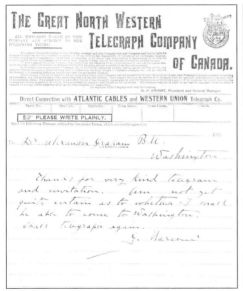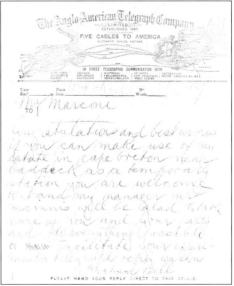

12. Cables exchanged between Alexander Graham Bell and Marconi, December 1901.
(Photograph: Marconi plc)

13. s.s. *Lake Champlain* – the first ocean-going ship to be fitted
with Marconi's wireless equipment, 1901.
(Photograph: Marconi plc)

14. s.s. *Lucania* – the first Cunard ship to be fitted with
wireless telegraphy equipment, June 1901.
(Photograph: Marconi plc)

15. The s.s. *Philadelphia*, in which, in October 1902, readable messages were received from Poldhu up to a distance of 1,551 miles, and test letters as far as 2,009 miles.
(Photograph: Marconi plc)

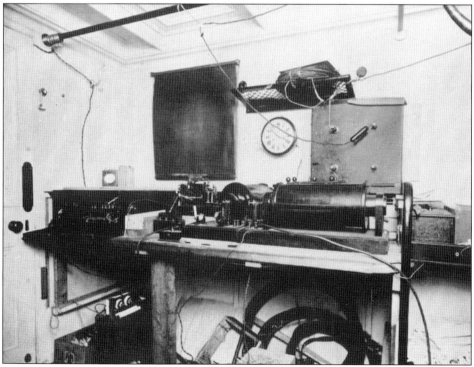

16. The Wireless Room on the s.s. *Philadelphia*.
(Photograph: Marconi plc)

In January 1903 the station at Cape Cod was used to transmit the first messages to Glace Bay in Newfoundland, where they could be re-transmitted to Poldhu. On 18th January, the first message to be received from North America to the UK was heard at Poldhu. However, the link proved to be very unreliable and broke down altogether when the aerial at Glace Bay collapsed under the weight of ice.

By 1905 a new aerial system was developed in the form of a long horizontal wire instead of the complicated cone structure of wires. However, the site at Poldhu was too restricted to allow the construction of a suitable inverted 'L' aerial, so a new station was set up at Clifden in Galway. Finally, in order to reduce as far as possible the length of telegraph landlines both in the UK and North America to facilitate traffic between London and New York, where most of the traffic occurred, stations were set up as near to those cities as possible At the UK end the site chosen was near the village of Waunfawr, not far from Caernarfon in North Wales.

All these early stations were on long waves, somewhere around 350 to 400 metres, and it was not until 1905 that Fleming introduced the wave-

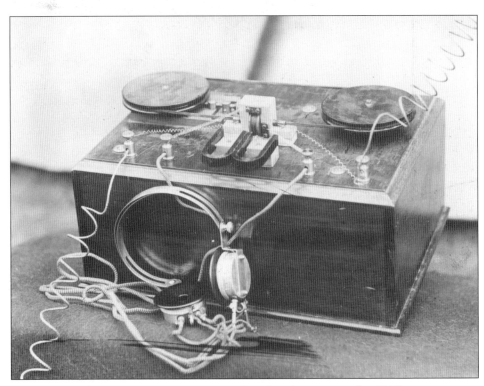

17. An early magnetic detector (hand-made prototyped, c.1903).
(Photograph: Marconi plc)

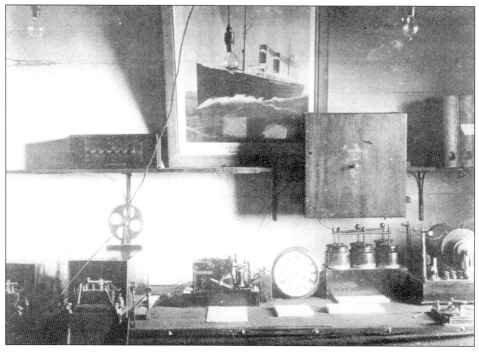

18. The interior of Marconi's station at the Lizard, c.1903.
(Photograph: Marconi plc)

19. Marconi's station at the Lizard, 1911.
(Photograph: Marconi plc)

meter which could be used to measure radio frequencies. By the early 20s experiments were well under way to develop the use of short waves, by means of which long distances could be covered with much smaller power. The key to this lay in overcoming propagation difficulties due to fading and the need to choose the most appropriate frequencies for any given time of day.

Eventually, by the mid-20s, short wave beamed services were set up by the Marconi Company, which linked London with the major cities of the world. In 1929, at the instigation of the Government, the Marconi Company was deprived of its control over British land stations, which were handed over to the General Post Office. Subsequently, the beam and cable services were combined into Cable and Wireless Ltd. Thereafter, the Marconi Company was a purely manufacturing company.

From 1902 onwards the fittings of both land and sea stations by the Marconi Company began to increase exponentially. Coast stations were established at the following sites in the UK: Crookhaven, Holyhead, Niton, Caister, Malin Head, Rosslare, Lizard, North Foreland, Withernsea and Innistrahull, and it was not long before they were followed by others.

Overseas stations were set up at: Belle Isle and Chateau Bay in the Gulf of St Lawrence, Babylon and Sagaonack in the USA, and on the Borkum Lightship and Lighthouse in Germany.

Importantly, Lloyds of London placed orders to equip their signal stations at Scilly, Flannan Island, Butt of Lewis, Cape Spartel, Port Said and Suez. This was a particularly useful development because before wireless tele-graphy was available communication between these stations and passing ships had to be conducted by flag signals, which often meant a consider-able detour and sometimes having to navigate close to a dangerous coast.

By 1911 certainly most of the shipping companies who operated passenger services had arranged for their vessels to be fitted and from then on, especially under pressure from Lloyds, the practice spread to cargo ships, tankers and other craft.

There is an interesting story contained in the *Marconigraph*, the house magazine first published by the Marconi Company in April 1911 (which later became the *Wireless World*) of the Premier of New Zealand who also has a claim to be an early Radio Officer. Some time circa 1909, this gentle-man happened to be travelling on an ocean liner (its name is not given) and had occasion to address a wireless telegram to the UK Chancellor of the Exchequer and Postmaster General urging them to forthwith introduce a penny postage to the United States. It so happened that he had begun life as a telegraph officer, and his old skill had not deserted him, for he sat

20. Receiving a broadcast from Poldhu on the s.s. *Victorian*, 1920.
(Photograph: Marconi plc)

down in the wireless cabin and tapped out the message himself on the Morse key.

When wireless was first fitted on ships its operators were immediately perceived as the custodians of a mysterious apparatus apparently devoted to generating sparks, and from that day forth the Radio Officer (as the wireless operator subsequently became known) was invariably addressed on board as 'Sparks'. As the author can recall, one did not not need a name; to everyone from the Captain to the cabin boy you were just 'Sparks', and so it remained until the species vanished into history. It was a happy arrangement, for on joining a new ship one found oneself familiarly so addressed by everyone, and less of a stranger than would otherwise be the case. One was left alone in the Radio Room to get on with one's arcane activities with a pleasing sense of individuality.

Before leaving the subject of Sparks, Mr Ronald Irving related in an article in the magazine *Radio Bygones*, June/July 1991, that a friend of his – an ex-Signals Petty Officer in the Royal Navy – reminisced that he had some-times been drunk on watch. This had not been deliberate but produced by the fumes generated by the old spark gaps, which were quenched with methylated spirits, and induced drowsiness.

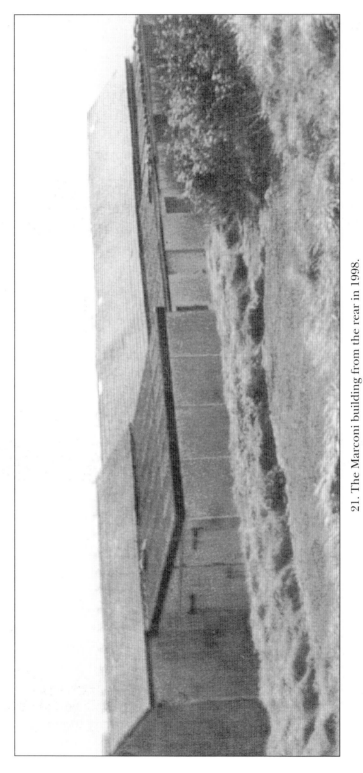

21. The Marconi building from the rear in 1998.
(Photograph: Courtney Rowe, Lizard)

EARLY WIRELESS TELEGRAPHY-FITTED SHIPS

22. The Isle of Man Steam Packet Company's ship *Empress Green*, 1906.
(Photograph: Marconi plc)

23. The Anchor liner *Caledonia*, 1906.
(Photograph: Marconi plc)

24. The Canadian Pacific Company's liner *Empress of Britain*, 1906.
(Photograph: Marconi plc)

25. The Booth liner *Antony*, 1907.
(Photograph: Marconi plc)

26. The first oil tanker to be fitted, in 1907, the *Iroquois*,
owned by the Anglo-American Oil Co.
(Photograph: Marconi plc)

27. The Royal Mail liner *Araguaya*, 1908.
(Photograph: Marconi plc)

28. The P&O liner *Malwa*, 1908.
(Photograph: Marconi plc)

29. The Orient liner *Otranto*, 1909.
(Photograph: Marconi plc)

30. The Union-Castle liner *Balmoral Castle*, 1909.
(Photograph: Marconi plc)

31. The s.s. *Oslo*, 1909.
(Photograph: Marconi plc)

32. The Bibby Line's *Gloucestershire*, 1909.
(Photograph: Marconi plc)

33. The Donaldson Line's *Saturnia*, 1909.
(Photograph: Marconi plc)

34. The s.s. *Princess Clementine*, showing the wireless cabin built between the funnels.
(Photograph: Marconi plc)

CHAPTER 2

The Training Schools
– Dots and Dashes Everywhere!

THE TWO BASIC REQUIREMENTS for a Radio Officer were the ability to send and receive in the Morse Code and operate the equipment involved. They also had to be acquainted with the Postmaster General's Regulations regarding the formation, transmission and charging of telegrams. A speed of twenty-five words per minute was demanded; higher speeds were attainable but the need to transcribe the message legibly kept the upper limit down to about twenty-five or less. And simple though the equipment was, it still represented a leap into a new discipline.

Coherers and spark gaps were temperamental, and frequently required finicky adjustments; signals were often very weak, and subject to interference due to atmospherics and fading. Very little was known about the propagation of radio waves and how they behaved, except that very early on it was perceived that greater distances could be achieved after dark. Aerial circuits required tuning, and electrical machines had to be started up and shut down in the correct manner or they would burn out.

Fortunately, there already existed a large pool of telegraphists trained for the land-line services, who only needed instruction on the elements of wireless telegraphy and the equipment used on board. The Morse Code, named after Samuel Finley Breese Morse (1791-1872), had come into its own after the American Congress had initiated a telegraph line between Washington and Boston.

The first wireless school to come into existence was established by the Marconi International Marine Communication Company at its Liverpool depot in 1903, and trained applicants from scratch, including the Morse Code. It was later transferred to Crosby Road, Seaforth, and Plate 35 shows Mr F. Jones, the Chief Instructor at the school in full uniformed splendour, including a Marconi cap badge. He seems an impressive character with a fierce-looking waxed moustache and coruscating pince-nez. An ex-Radio

Officer who had served as chief Radio Officer of the *Lusitania,* among other vessels, his Junker-like appearance suggests that his students would have had their noses kept closely applied to the grind-stone.

The course of instruction consisted of:

35. Mr F. Jones, Wireless Instructor at the Marconi School, Liverpool.
(Photograph: Marconi plc)

1. Elementary electricity and magnetism.
2. Fundamental principles of wireless tele-graphy.
3. Transmitting by practice buzzer sets and receiving by head telephones.
4. The various pieces and types of apparatus used and associated diagrams of electrical connections.
5. The connecting up of the various parts, comprising complete sets, how to trace faults and repair breakdowns.
6. Rules and regulations laid down by the Radiotelegraph Convention for the commercial working of wireless telegraphy.
7. Clerical work in connection with telegraphic accounts and returns.
8. General routine and discipline aboard ship.

At the end of the course the students were required to sit an examination conducted by the Postmaster General, after which they went to sea, usually commencing as a junior Radio Officer.

By 1912, the Marconi Marine Company had set up a special school in London, at their Head Office in the Strand, to train applicants who already had telegraphic experience. It was, in fact, a sort of finishing school for telegraphists who wished to acquire a knowledge of wireless telegraphy, and go to sea as a Radio Officer in the company's employ.

There were three classes of qualification for Radio Officers, all Certificates issued by the Postmaster General after the candidate had passed the appropriate examination: First, Second and Special. Details of the syllabus would be boring to the reader, but basically they covered, at three different levels, a knowledge of the Morse Code – twenty-five words per minute for the First Class; twenty for the Second, the necessary theory to understand how the equipment functioned and how to maintain it, and the operating procedures and International Regulations which governed the handling of messages.

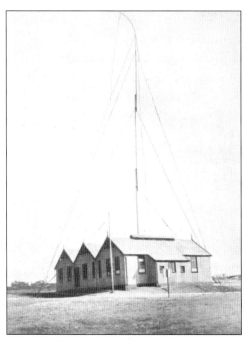

36. The first Marconi Service Depot,
Seaforth Sands, Liverpool, 1903.
(Photograph: Marconi plc)

37. The School Room at the Marconi Depot, Seaforth Sands, Liverpool, 1903.
(Photograph: Marconi plc)

38. The Training Room, Marconi House, London.
(Photograph: Marconi plc)

39. The Instrument Room, Marconi House, London.
(Photograph: Marconi plc)

In the late 1960s the British General Post Office introduced a revised Marine General Radio Certificate which replaced the previous First and Second Class Certificates, although the Special Certificate was retained, mainly to cover the requirements on trawlers. At the same time the Morse speed for the new certificate was reduced to twenty words per minute. It recognised that the average speed of working at sea was probably about twenty to twenty-two words per minute, and Second Class Certificates predominated anyway.

At the same time, other changes and related qualifications were introduced which took account of the increasing complexity of not just radio equipment, but electronic equipment on ships generally. Chief of these was Radar, introduced during World War II, which became general on all ships, and eventually escalated to the point where most carried two radars. These steadily became more complicated, incorporating various kinds of built-in navigational aids. At first the training situation was covered by training courses provided by the various manufacturers of radar equipment, who usually issued their own diplomas. This somewhat unsatisfactory situation was resolved when the Ministry of Transport, in conjunction with the Merchant Navy Training Board, instituted the Ministry of Transport Radar Maintenance Certificate. This involved a searching practical examination on two representative radars of different makes, and two comprehensive theory papers of a high standard.

Finally came the Marine Electronic Officers Certificate, which covered the whole range of electronic equipment likely to be encountered on board ship, the starting off point being the standard PMG Certificate. This certificate was issued by the Merchant Navy Training Board, and was intended to equip Radio Officers with the necessary skills to maintain any equipment, not just in the Radio Room, but also the various types of navigational aids fitted on the bridge, and electronic equipment in the engine room.

During World War II new entrants could only sit for the Special Certificate, which entitled them to go to sea as junior Radio Officers – all ships in war-time had to carry three officers in order to provide a 24-hour radio watch service. Working at sea was confined to reception, since transmission would enable the German Intelligence to locate convoys or isolated ships. The Special Certificate could then, after six months service at sea, be converted to a Second Class Certificate by sitting an appropriate written theory paper at one of various centres set up by the Postmaster General, usually in a major port. With this Certificate a Radio Officer could then take charge of a ship station, except on a passenger ship, on his own. Conversions to First Class were also possible during war-time, but this involved a Morse test

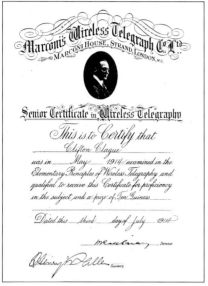

40. A Marconi Cerificate
of Proficiency, 1914.
(Photograph: Marconi plc)

at the higher speed of twenty-five words per minute and a written theory paper at a higher level.

There was no lack of recruits to the new service. The rates of pay were higher than those paid to telegraphists in the Post Office and cable services, and also increased more rapidly, rising to £2.15 per week with all found on board. In the first decade of the 19th century this was quite substantial. There was the prospect of visiting foreign countries and, in that pre-container age when ships were loaded and unloaded by cranes and derricks, they might be in port for weeks at a time. In the early days in particular, all kinds of interesting sea-going appointments existed; on the great Western Ocean liners, cargo ships of every description, large steam yachts, foreign warships and even on airships!

After serving at sea for some years there was the possibility of a shore appointment with the company, either at Head Office, or at one of the many servicing depots set up in the UK and all around the world. The list of Radio Officers who achieved distinction in their later careers is almost endless, and includes such distinguished names as Sir William Haley, Director of the BBC, Sir Ernest Fisk, Managing Director of EMI (listed in an early edition of the Marconi Company's 'General Orders' 1913, in the author's possession, as Resident Inspector in Sydney, New South Wales), David Sarnoff, President of the Radio Corporation of America, and Albert Ginman, President of the Canadian Marconi Company. And not to be forgotten is Radio Officer Jack Binns of *Titanic* fame (see chapter 4) who became the President of the Hazeltine Electronic Corporation of New York.

There was a growing demand for Radio Officers, and it was not long before private training colleges began to spring up to cater for the numbers of young men attracted by the new service. They were scattered all over the country, mostly in the neighbourhood of the large ports, but many inland. Then by the late 20s, Technical Colleges began to offer training courses leading to the PMG Certificates of Proficiency in Wireless Telegraphy. After World War II, these increased enormously in number, until at nearly every

45

major port around the entire United Kingdom the local Technical College offered marine training courses.

To mention all of them is precluded by space, and instead some representative examples of the best known have been selected. This has been an invidious choice for the writer, who was connected for over twelve years with their organisation, the Association of Marine Wireless Colleges, and well acquainted with the high standards and excellent training offered by all of them.

To begin with the private schools, three particularly well-known ones were the Wireless College, Colwyn Bay, the London Telegraph Training College, and the North East School of Wireless Telegraphy, which served the North East coast.

THE LONDON TELEGRAPH TRAINING COLLEGE, EARL'S COURT

This was one of the earliest and best known private schools in the United Kingdom, and the author is indebted to David Evans, its last proprietor, for much of the information which follows, and other fascinating material relating to the early history of wireless communication in this country.

41. The British School of Telegraphy, 1908.
(Photograph: David Evans)

42. Two generations of owners of the British School of Wireless Telegraphy
– Idris Evans and his son, David Evans.
(Photograph: David Evans)

The college began life as the London Telegraph Training College (later to be amalgamated with the British School of Wireless Telegraphy, established in 1897) and became known as the London Electronics College. Finally, as the British School of Wireless Telegraphy, it continued various proprietors until 1988 when it was sold by the last in the line, David Evans, whose father had become proprietor in 1956. The trail of ownership down the years becomes as complicated as the family tree of the Vanderbilts; it divides into two separately owned establishments which later re-unite again, with a short-lived off-shoot in Rugby during the late 50s. Different proprietors appear, vanish and then re-appear. Only the explanatory diagram (page 48), kindly drawn by David Evans, clears up the confusion. It is included here more for its historic interest than its intrinsic value.

The college trained many Radio Officers who achieved fame in later life, including Harold Bride, the surviving Radio Officer of the *Titanic*, who qualified in July 1911. It enjoyed a high reputation from the start and the author, who had a great deal to do with the Inspector of Wireless Telegraphy's department during the 60s and 70s, recalls one of the examiners, Arnold Whalley, particularly praising both the Earls Court School and Colwyn Bay for the excellence of their training, remarking that many of the private

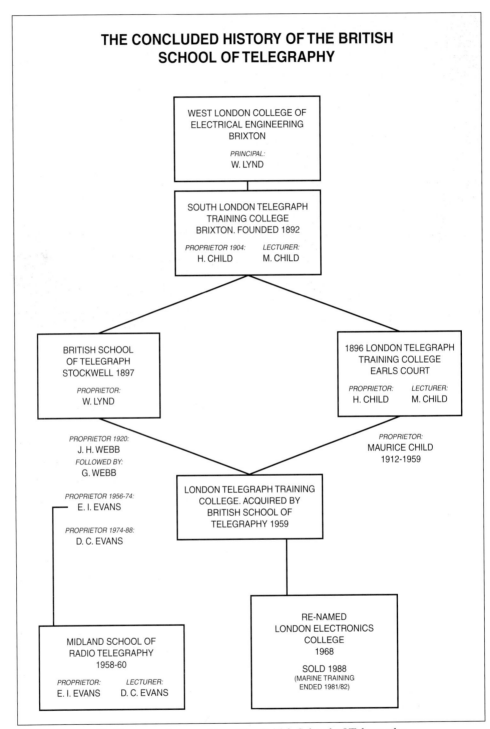

THE CONCLUDED HISTORY OF THE BRITISH SCHOOL OF TELEGRAPHY

WEST LONDON COLLEGE OF ELECTRICAL ENGINEERING BRIXTON

PRINCIPAL:
W. LYND

SOUTH LONDON TELEGRAPH TRAINING COLLEGE BRIXTON. FOUNDED 1892

PROPRIETOR 1904:   *LECTURER:*
H. CHILD   M. CHILD

BRITISH SCHOOL OF TELEGRAPH STOCKWELL 1897

PROPRIETOR:
W. LYND

1896 LONDON TELEGRAPH TRAINING COLLEGE EARLS COURT

PROPRIETOR: *LECTURER:*
H. CHILD   M. CHILD

PROPRIETOR 1920:
J. H. WEBB
FOLLOWED BY:
G. WEBB

PROPRIETOR:
MAURICE CHILD
1912-1959

PROPRIETOR 1956-74:
E. I. EVANS

PROPRIETOR 1974-88:
D. C. EVANS

LONDON TELEGRAPH TRAINING COLLEGE. ACQUIRED BY BRITISH SCHOOL OF TELEGRAPHY 1959

MIDLAND SCHOOL OF RADIO TELEGRAPHY 1958-60

PROPRIETOR: *LECTURER:*
E. I. EVANS   D. C. EVANS

RE-NAMED LONDON ELECTRONICS COLLEGE 1968

SOLD 1988
(MARINE TRAINING ENDED 1981/82)

43. Changes of ownership of the British School of Telegraphy.
(Diagram by David Evans)

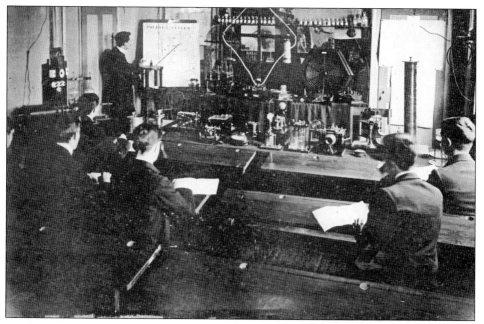

44. Instrument Room, British School of Telegraphy, 1908.
(Photograph: David Evans)

schools offered training of a concentrated nature which could well serve as a model for elsewhere.

Typical of these, in the high flowing language of the day, redolent with such phrases as 'your esteemed order will receive our immediate attention, and we trust that our moderate charges and attention to business will continue to merit your valued support', etc., the proud owner addressed the following portentous notice to the public:

> To Parents and Guardians desirous of placing their sons or wards in a position above that of the average mercantile or bank clerk, few, if any, vocations at the present day offer better prospects than that of telegraphy, and the specialised training given by the London Telegraph Training College Ltd., (the oldest and largest of its kind in the United Kingdom), is in the unique position of being able to obtain for its students positions that cannot be obtained elsewhere. The college not only provides the necessary training, but owing to its intimate connection with the principal Cable and Wireless Telegraph Companies, is uniquely able to obtain for its students a lucrative position in either service immediately they are qualified to accept

them, at a commencing remuneration of from £100 to £200 per annum.

The College possesses TWO WIRELESS TELEGRAPH STATIONS fitted with the type of apparatus supplied by the Marconi Wireless Telegraph Company Ltd., and has been recognised by the Company as a recruiting source for operators desirous of entering its service.

The other wireless college which can share pride of place with the London Telegraph Training College was the Wireless College, Colwyn Bay.

Countless Radio Officers, including the author, began their careers there, attracted by the high pressure national advertising campaign set in motion by its indefatigable proprietor, Gordon S. Whale, whose commercial acumen must have been of epic proportions.

Gordon Whale received his training with the Direct Spanish Telegraph Company in 1912 and joined the Marconi Wireless Telegraph Company in 1916. His first appointment was at their station at Clifden on the west coast of Ireland, and then in 1917 he was transferred to their station near Caernarfon in North Wales.

45. The Wireless College, Colwyn Bay.
(Photograph: 'Radio Bygones' & A. N. Smith, an ex-student)

46. Advertisement for the Wireless College, Colwyn Bay.
(Photograph: 'Radio Bygones' & A. N. Smith, an ex-student)

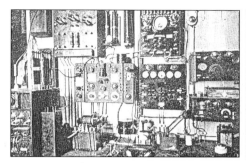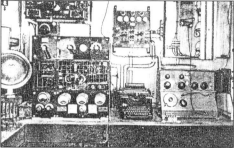

47. The training equipment, Wireless College, Colwyn Bay, late 30s.
(Photographs courtesy Kenneth Pizey)

In 1918, while still employed by the Marconi Company, he opened a school for training wireless operators at Caernarfon, as a profitable side-line. When this came to the notice of his employers they offered him the choice of closing down the school or resigning, and he chose the latter. In 1920 he moved it to Colwyn Bay and, in 1923, established it in a large detached house in East Parade. The building has long since been pulled down, and now the M55 expressway traffic thunders over the spot where once radio officer students pounded morse keys and absorbed the fundamentals of wireless communication.

In 1926 he appointed an ex-Marine Radio Officer, Charles Oliver, as Instructor, who was later joined by an assistant, Harry Nelson, known in the author's time at the college as 'Tubby Nelson'. In 1935 Gordon Whale returned to London but in 1937 established another school in an old country house – Loperwood Manor, at Calmore, near Southampton, and sent down Harry Nelson to run it. It was an ambitious project, entirely worthy of its creator, whose aim, apparently, was to create a sort of Pangbourne of Wireless Telegraphy. The author dimly remembers seeing a photograph in its advertising brochure, taken in front of the school, with serried ranks of students clad in Merchant Navy uniforms drawn up in parade formation. In front, on a sort of rostrum, stood Gordon Whale, resplendent in full uniform with four gold bands of his own devising and wearing a peaked cap complete with scrambled eggs, taking the salute. It was a good idea and deserved more success than it achieved, for it was closed down in 1940 when the Admiralty requisitioned the building.

The tuition at Colwyn Bay was a no-nonsense basic affair and honed to push all but the dullest students through the Postmaster General's examination for radio officers. The College also prepared students for the City & Guilds examinations in Radio Communication, grades Preliminary, Inter-

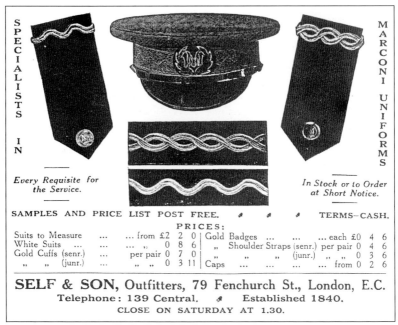

SPECIALISTS IN		**MARCONI UNIFORMS**

Every Requisite for the Service.

In Stock or to Order at Short Notice.

SAMPLES AND PRICE LIST POST FREE. ✈ ✈ ✈ TERMS—CASH.

PRICES:

Suits to Measure ...	... from £2 2 0	Gold Badges ...	...	...each £0	4 6
White Suits	... ,. 0 8 6	„ Shoulder Straps (senr.) per pair 0			4 6
Gold Cuffs (senr.) ...	per pair 0 7 0	„ „ „ (junr.) ,. „ 0			3 6
„ „ (junr.) ...	„ „ 0 3 11	Caps	... from 0		2 6

SELF & SON, Outfitters, 79 Fenchurch St., London, E.C.
Telephone: 139 Central. ✈ Established 1840.
CLOSE ON SATURDAY AT 1.30.

48. Uniform advertisement, *Wireless World*, c.1912.
(Photograph: Marconi plc)

mediate, and Final; the latter being a very respectable qualification for a shore-based career, as well as at sea.

During the author's period at Colwyn Bay it was war-time and the students were drawn from a wide range of backgrounds. They included a Prince Oblensky, who had arrived from the *Conway*, and another of Russian origin whose name she cannot remember except that he was popularly referred to as 'Rasputin'. Hugh Lloyd, who later achieved national fame on the stage and television, was a prominent performer in the college's custom-built theatre, where shows were put on for the townsfolk of Colwyn Bay. And very good they were. One act was done by an Irishman who stood on his hands and drank a glass of water, and then played a tune on a saw. And at least one student later inherited the family stately home (see page 53).

The author has vivid recollections of both the college and the town. It was mercifully out of the flight path of German bombers on their way to Liverpool, and to her, as is common with people of a certain age who look back, the sun always seemed to be shining.

A large part of the students' time was spent in practising the Morse Code, and they perambulated around the town at lunch time with tele-phone headsets draped round their necks, rather like the stethoscopes that

52

```
W I R E L E S S   C O L L E G E   T H E A T R E.   C O L W Y N  B A Y.

PROGRAMME.                  S P A R K S.                 Price 3d.

Principal Gordon S. Mile, F.R.S.A., A.M.I.R.E. etc., Presents a

VaRIETY PERFORMANCE by The Wireless College Students.          *
      February 10th, 11th, 12th 13th and 14th at 7:30pm. Matinee Saturday 2: 0pm.
                  Compere:  Hugh Lloyd (The rising comedy star)

  1. "The Fleet's in Port" and on board is the entire Company.

  2. "The Perfect Day" Three Cameos featuring Bill Kenyon - Spark of Sparks.

  3. Roger Frisby (B.B.C. Swing Trumpeter) and his band.
                        Vocal: Miss Megan Jones.
  4. Jim Noakes - The Shropshire Lad.

  5. "King of Caructus", featuring A. Martin; P.Thomas; J.Noakes: B.Kenyon.

  6. David Rose - and his violin.

  7. Paddy Lawrence - Ireland's gift to Britain.

  8. Wireless College Swing Band - Vocal by Miss Megan Jones.

  9. Arthur Webber in popular Songs.

 10. "Keep Moving" featuring Hugh Lloyd & Company.

                        I N T E R V A L.

 11. "On the Good Ship Victory V" - an original radio commentary taking
         you on board that happy vessel.
         Hugh Lloyd - Commentator.        Roger Frisby - Captain.
         Bill Kenyon - Sparks.    Jim Noakes - Bosun.   Alan Martin 1st mate.
         P. Chamberlain - Cook,   P. Lawrence - 2nd Mate. P. Finney -Engineer
         P. Thomas - Deck Hand.   Misses Looker I.; Hughes D.; & Rickards H.
         Messrs. Look A., Gatley D., Stewart D., Stevenson A., & Liddell A.

 12. Roger Frisby and his swing band hold a piano audition.

 13. Bill Kenyon & Peter Thomas - "Sparks and Oliver Wakefield.

 14. Roger Frisby and his band. Vocal by Miss Megan Jones.

 15. Hugh Lloyd - variety, revue, & cabaret Artist.

 16. FINALE. Victory V. An original Song by Stan Masters.
                        GOD SAVE THE KING.

 Piano Accompanist.... Mr. R. Boll.  Stage Manager.... R. White.
              Assistant Stage Manager:  A. Bernstein.

     The whole show written and produced by Hugh Lloyd - the Compere.

 All proceeds, without deductions of any kind, to be handed over to

 H.M. Chancellor of Exchequer as a free gift for War Weapons.

 Coffee will be served during the interval.

                        Thank you for your support.
                            * Also 29 to 2f March 1942
```

49. 'Sparks' theatrical programme for the 'Variety Performance'
at the Theatre of the Wireless College, Colwyn Bay, February 1942.
(Courtesy Kenneth Pizey)

separate medical students from ordinary mortals. The Morse classroom, presided over by the Chief Instructor, Dusty Miller, was a large room fitted with long wooden tables with correspondingly long benches on either side. At the end of each table was a Morse key and an oscillator, whose output was connected to two wires running the length of the bench on either side, to which the students could attach their telephones with crocodile clips. At first the Morse instructor tapped out suitable material and later the students would take it each in turn to send to the others.

Theory classes were conducted by Charles Oliver in a large wooden shed, built for the purpose in the garden; he was a tall, gangly individual with a pronounced north country accent rather like the man in the Murray Mint television advertisement of years ago. He used to enliven his lectures with anecdotes of life at sea, such as playing chess by radio to while away a long, slow crossing of the Pacific. Our principal textbook was the *Admiralty Handbook of Wireless Telegraphy*, Volumes I and II, and Charles Oliver not only knew them off by heart, but possessed the gift of reducing them to the clearest of lecture notes. The author gratefully remembers them and also sitting the examination at Colwyn Bay for the City & Guilds Radio Communication Examinations, at which, to the surprise of the class, Charles appeared to sit it with us, unscrewing a large fountain pen with an inscrutable smile.

The actual equipment, which the students were expected to operate during their examination by an examiner appointed by the Postmaster General, was housed in a sort of technical shrine adapted from a hallway leading to the School Office. It was of the most basic kind; a valve transmitter whose glass valve seemed to stare out from behind a metal grid like the goggle of an Edwardian diving suit, a receiver, direction-finder and a device called an auto-alarm. This was a clever arrangement which could respond to a special signal always sent out before an SOS message, and alert Radio Officers off duty on other ships within range. There was also a spark transmitter, and various supporting items like battery charging boards.

Until a few weeks before the examination, the students were only allowed to look at the equipment and draw pictures of it for their notebooks. These were supplemented by diagrams of the electrical circuit connections, expounded upon by Chas Oliver in his wooden hut.

The equipment was rented from the Marconi International Marine Company, because they made sure that that was the only way it could be obtained. The company's early financial arrangements, which miraculously survived until shipowners cottoned on to it after the Second World War, must have been one of the most ingenious devices ever invented by a wily accountant. But of course, in the beginning, the company held the patents and monopoly, and could do more or less what it liked.

All the equipment was hired out on a rental-maintenance contract which stipulated three months payment in advance. This was profitably consolidated by the company's policy of paying its bills three months in arrears whenever they could get away with it. Radio Officers were hired out at a substantial profit on the same terms. Until the late 30s, the equipment was so simple and rugged that it was almost indestructible, apart from running replacements like valves, fuses and electrical contacts.

The return in capital investment must have been enormous; a spark transmitter could easily remain in a ship for twenty-five years earning a good rental, the first six months of which probably paid for the transmitter. The author recalls working on the Bar Light Vessel in the Mersey sometime in 1950, which had an early radio beacon and radio-telephone set still functioning and earning revenue after nearly thirty years of service.

The college was a boarding establishment, and during the author's time there, war-time shortages and restrictions made catering difficult. Yet her recollection is of plain wholesome food, bread and margarine ad lib, and particularly tasty sweets in the form of various forms of sticky duff, lubricated by thick yellow custard. Cups were not available, but that was no problem for the resourceful Gordon Whale, who solved the situation with empty glass jam-jars which could be refilled ad lib from huge metal kettles.

The school and the town remains framed forever in the author's memory, in a sort of golden vision of optimistic youth, and adventures which lay ahead. Occasionally, ex-students who lived locally would visit the school on leave from sea, resplendent in uniforms and with tales of convoys, submarines, being torpedoed and visiting romantic places against the background of the war at sea.

As the 30s drew on, training for Radio Officers began to be provided by the Technical Colleges which were to be found in all the main ports of the United Kingdom, and post World War II most of these offered courses. As with the private colleges, it would be pointless to list them all. Perhaps the Hull Municipal Technical College might be a good example because the service it provided was so closely tied up with the very life-blood of the port. Indeed, the same can be said of the college at Grimsby, and of others at the various ports, but space precludes their inclusion.

Like so many institutions of its kind, the Hull College sprang from a Mechanics Institute, which in turn owed its existence to a local Philosophic and Literary Society, and was set up in 1823 in Charlotte Street. Following the 1888 Local Government Act, local councils were encouraged to set up Municipal Technical Schools, and from this the present college emerged. Radio training began there the early 1930s, triggered by the fact that Hull was a major port, and also because of the rapidly growing importance attached to wireless communication, especially to trawlers, so vital to the whole area.

Plate 50 shows the training equipment installed in the college at about this time. It is typical of the period, with an early valve transmitter on the extreme left, and what looks to the author like a Marconi 341¼ Kw Quench Gap transmitter on the right. In the middle is a 379 Direction Finder and a 352 two valve receiver, while charging boards with carbon filament lamps to drop the voltage are screwed to the wall. For the author this picture is

50. Marine radio training equipment, Hull Technical College, circa early 30s.
(Photograph: Hull College of Technology)

enormously nostalgic, for it appears to contain all the equipment fitted on the s.s. *Lorca* owned by Cory Brothers, in which she went down to West Africa in the early part of 1943; a voyage made somewhat exciting by the activities of U-boats then operating out of Vichy-French controlled Dakar (see page 124).

A contemporary description of the course then available at the Hull College is given below, because it seems to carry a special flavour of those years:

COURSES AVAILABLE AT THE MUNICIPAL TECHNICAL COLLEGE

In addition to the installations shown on the opposite page, the College has a complete Aircraft Transmitter and Receiver of the type used for examinations at Croydon Airport, a complete 60-watt Radio Telephone Transmitter and receiver of the type used on trawlers, and equipment for servicing broadcast receivers.

For those desirous of sailing on trawlers. Time required about six months. Tuition Fee: 4 guineas.

For those desirous of sailing on foreign going vessels. Time required about 12 months. Fee for 1st Class: 10 guineas, for 2nd Class: 7 guineas.

Deals with the theoretical part of the First and Second Class examinations. This course provides lesson and test papers, text-books, and corrections by Tutor. The course is intended for trawler operators who wish to obtain a superior Certificate, or for those who cannot afford to stay in Hull for the full length of time normally required for preparation for the First or Second Class examination.

For those desirous of entering Imperial Airways as operators on Air Liners. Tuition fee: 10 guineas. Time required about 12 months.

For those desirous of entering the works of a radio manufacturing company. Tuition C.G.L.I: 10 guineas, I.E.E.: 14 guineas.

For those who already hold the London Matriculation Certificate, and who wish to enter the general electrical or mechanical industries. Full particulars on application to the Principal.

The fees cover full instruction until the Certificate is obtained. A corresponding reduction is made to those holding Special or Second Class P.M.G. Certificates.

It is not generally appreciated that Lord Louis Mountbatten specialised in wireless communication between the wars, and by 1929, as a Lieutenant Commander, he was in charge of signals instruction at the signals school in Portsmouth. As Philip Zeigler mentions in his biography of Mountbatten, 'people were overwhelmed by the lucidity with which he expounded these arcane and complex subjects. He knew the value of cultivating certain eccentricities, always prefacing his remarks when turning to the blackboard with a sonorous, "Watch me – observe!" '

He did not merely teach the syllabus, he reformed it. He set up a drawing school to produce simple standardised diagrams of every circuit, and ensured that they were incorporated, with his own explanations, in the *Handbook of Wireless Telegraphy*, Volumes I and II. As another valuable feature, certain paragraphs throughout the work were asterisked and printed in small print. These dealt with more advanced descriptions of radio theory, which could be omitted by a student wishing to only cover the theory needed to provide a good basic knowledge of wireless communication, without interrupting the flow of the argument.

This seems to the author to be a typical contribution from a fresh mind, and Lord Louis's connection with these volumes deserves recording, together with his connection with the development of radio in the Royal Navy. Another consideration concerns the contribution made by Admiral Sir Henry Jackson, KCVO, FRS (1855-1929), to the development of radio communication at sea. It was not until 1963 that material on Captain Jackson's (as he was then) pioneer work came to more prominent light. He was an officer of considerable experience, who had commanded the Naval Torpedo School, and while in that capacity had carried out his own experiments into the use of Hertzian waves for the purpose of wireless communication. He met with Marconi in 1896 and each discovered that they had been working along the same lines, unknown to each other. It is nice to relate that, in spite of what might have been perceived as an element of competition between them, this did not stand in the way of establishing a long period of friendship and mutual collaboration. But it does indicate that Marconi perhaps has to share, to a greater or lesser extent, some of the credit for the early development of wireless at sea, both in the MN and RN with Admiral Jackson.

The post World War II years saw a large increase in the numbers of Radio Officer students, and the same years brought increasing sophistication to the equipment used at sea, which by then included radar as standard, and the college training facilities were updated accordingly. But by the late 80s the decline in the British Merchant Navy that had been caused by the advent of air travel, container ships and competition from foreign-owned vessels sailing under flags of convenience, had spelled the end of the Radio Officer at sea. An era had come to an end, and with it the need for specialised training based on Morse communication at sea.

With this diminishing demand for Radio Officers, the Association of Marine Radio Colleges, in conjunction with the Merchant Navy Training Board, agreed to cease training and examining for and issuing the Marine Radio General Certificate in 1992. Meanwhile the UK Merchant Shipping (Radio Installations) 1992 permitted vessels currently in service and those yet to be built (up to January 1995) to operate a radio-telegraph installation on board until 31st February 1999, with the consequential requirement for a Radio Officer. Vessels declared by the owner to be taken out of service not later than two years beyond that date were allowed to continue as radio-telegraph ship until the 31st January 2001.

These arrangements were linked to the UK signing up to the IMO Convention implementing the carriage of automatic Distress and Safety equipment such as EPIRB (Emergency Position Indicating Radio Beacon) and GMDSS (Global Maritime Distress Safety System) which then became required for international voyages. Countries who did not sign up to the IMO Convention of course remained free to make their own decisions and interpretation of the law.

CHAPTER 3

Pre-1914 – Sensation at Sea – Two Disasters
and the Capture of a Murderer

THE LOSS OF THE *REPUBLIC*

THE *REPUBLIC*, OWNED BY THE Oceanic Steamship Company of Liverpool (the White Star Line) sailed from New York on 22nd January 1909, with 250 first-class passengers, 211 steerage, and a crew of 300. About 175 miles west of the Ambrose Light she was in collision with the Italian steamer *Florida* at about 5.30 a.m. on 23rd January. The *Republic* suffered severe damage, which extended below the waterline, and the Radio Officer, Jack Binns, sent out a distress signal which was received by the coast station at Siasconcet on the American mainland. That station then broadcast news of the disaster, which alerted any suitably fitted ships which were within reach of the *Republic*.

Although the wireless cabin on the *Republic* had been badly damaged, and the ship's dynamos had stopped, plunging the vessel into darkness, Binn's equipment was still working from batteries, and he was able to keep in touch with other stations. The *Florida*, which was carrying 800 emigrants, mostly refugees from a recent earthquake in Italy, was still afloat. Her Master, Captain Ruspini, got in touch with Captain Sealby of the *Republic*, and between them they decided to transfer the passengers on the *Republic* to the *Florida*.

Binns had been busy at his key ever since the collision, and was able to report to Captain Sealby that several ships were coming to their rescue, including the *New York*, *Lorraine*, *Furnessia*, *Lucania* and *Baltic*. The latter was the first to arrive and it was then decided to transfer all the passengers from both vessels on to the *Baltic*, a hazardous operation which was completed without the loss of a single life. The *Baltic* then continued on her passage to New York, while in the meantime Captain Sealby decided to do what he could to save his ship.

59

51. R.M.S. *Baltic*. Painting by Tommy Sandham whilst serving on board as Radio Officer, 1931.
(*Photograph: Merseyside Maritime Museum*)

She was taken in tow by tugs summoned by Jack Binns, but when south of Martha's Vineyard began to sink rapidly, and the crew had to throw themselves into the water to escape. Captain Sealby remained with his ship, and searchlights from other vessels revealed him climbing up the foremast, to which he clung until it disappeared beneath the water. Amazingly, he and all his crew survived.

The author cannot do better than to record the public appreciation of the gallantry and professional skill demonstrated by all concerned in the affair by quoting from H. E. Hancock in his invaluable and authoritative book, *Wireless at Sea*, published in 1950:

> During the run in to New York from Nantucket, the passengers on board the *Baltic* collected a fund and then decided to strike medals from the proceeds. Among the passengers was a Mr Ingersoll, of the Ingersoll Watch Company, and he undertook to strike the medals and attend to their distribution. Four of the medals were struck in gold, and one each presented to the three Captains and Jack Binns. The medal bore on one side the letters CQD at the top, a picture of the ship in the centre, and underneath the name *Republic*.

52. Presentation by Marconi to Jack Binns, Radio Officer of the White Star Liner *Republic*.
(Photograph: Marconi plc)

On the other side the inscription read:

> From the saloon passengers of the RMS *Baltic* and RMS *Republic* to the
> officers and crews of the s.s. *Republic, Baltic* and *Florida* for gallantry,
> commemorating the rescue of over 1,700 souls, January 24th, 1909.

Mr H. G. Tattersall, the Radio Officer of the *Baltic*, had stayed by his instruments constantly without sleep for fifty-two hours. Similarly, Binns of the *Republic*, with the walls of of his radio cabin shattered by the bow of the *Florida*, stayed at his key all through the weary day sending out his distress call CQD. Upon this signal and the correct working of his instruments had depended the safety of all on board.

There was an exciting scene on the White Star Pier, New York, when Captain Sealby, of the *Republic*, and Jack Binns, the Radio Officer, landed on 26th January. Both were caught up by a number of enthusiastic seamen and stewards of the White Star Line, who carried them on their shoulders. The crowd was delirious with joy at the sight of these brave men. They marched out to the street blowing trumpets and, after exhibiting their heroes to a large throng of people assembled outside, headed about, returned to the pier, and deposited their by-this-time embarrassed burdens in the offices of the company. Much the same thing happened to Captain Ruspini, of the *Florida*, who succeeded in bringing his ship safely into dock.

Captain Sealby and Jack Binns returned to Liverpool in the *Baltic*. When the ship arrived at the Mersey port on 8th February a large crowd of relatives and friends gathered on the landing stage and the men were warmly greeted on stepping ashore. Particular attention was concentrated on Jack Binns. He was met by his sweetheart and several relatives from Peterborough, his home town, and many strangers in the crowd insisted in shaking hands with him. Binns, who again repeated that he had just done his duty, said he was going to London at once to fully report to the Marconi Directors.

He had an enthusiastic reception at Peterborough. Thousands of people assembled to greet him and he drove with the Mayor to the Guildhall where a number of prominent citizens met to do him honour. The Mayor presented him with an address of welcome from the Corporation expressing the pride the citizens felt in his heroism and their admiration of the coolness and promptitude with which he used the wireless apparatus.

The directors of the Marconi Wireless Telegraph Company held a reception at their offices at Watergate House, Adelphi, London, on 10th February

1909, at which Binns was presented with a gold watch. Among those present were Sir Charles Euan-Smith, Mr Marconi, Mr H. Jameson Davis, Major Flood Page and Mr Henry Saunders. Mr Marconi, who made the presentation, congratulated Binns upon having been the first to show what wireless telegraphy could do to save life at sea. Binns, in thanking the directors, said that he hoped he would always be able to do his duty in a similar way should the necessity unhappily recur.

Eventually, Jack Binns made his life and home in North America, where in the fullness of time he became the President of the Hazeltine Radio Corporation of New York.

THE ARREST OF DR CRIPPEN

The loss of the *Republic* fixed the attention of the world on the importance of wireless telegraphy as a means of rescue at sea, but in 1910 the arrest of Dr Crippen – entirely as a result of a wireless message – galvanised the world's press into exploitation of the new weapon now available to the streets of ink.

The details are so well-known that they scarcely merit repeating, but the sensational part played by wireless telegraphy deserves a place in this book, if only for completeness. To cover the details briefly, Crippen lost his nerve

53. CPS Liner *Montrose*
(Photograph: Marconi plc)

54. Dr Crippen and Ethel Le Neve aboard s.s. *Montrose.*

(Photograph: Marconi plc)

after being interrogated by the police, and fled the country, accompanied by his typist, Miss Ethel Le Neve. A few days afterwards parts of a woman's body were discovered buried beneath the floor of the cellar of Crippen's house and pictures of the couple were published widely in the press.

In the meantime, the pair had reached Antwerp, where they had sailed in the s.s. *Montrose* for Montreal. Miss Le Neve had cut her hair short, and both were entered on the passenger list as 'Mr Robinson and his son'. However, it was not long before the Master, Captain Kendall, realised that the couple bore a striking resemblance to the fugitives, and his suspicions were confirmed by the apparent ill-fitting of the boy's clothes,

55. The arrest of Dr Crippen – *Weekly Dispatch.*

(Photograph: Marconi plc)

but more particularly because the father was occasionally to squeeze the boy's hand more tenderly than would normally be expected to be the case.

He therefore, on 22nd July 1910, instructed his Radio Officer to send a message to the Canadian Pacific Railway Offices in Liverpool to say that he

56. Captain Kendall's marconigram advising that Crippen
and Ethel Le Neve were on board the *Montrose*.
(Photograph: New Scotland Yard)

57. The Canadian Pacific Liner *Montrose*.
(Photograph: Peabody Essex Museum, Salem, Massachusetts)

believed Crippen and Miss Le Neve were on board his vessel. They at once got in touch with Scotland Yard, who through various messages exchanged with the *Montrose* were able to confirm their suspicions. On Saturday, 23rd July, Chief Inspector Dew sailed for Montreal on the *Laurentic*, which was due to reach that port before the *Montrose*.

In that way began a race across the Atlantic upon which the world's press fastened in a sort of feeding frenzy. They were able to indulge in a field day, with maps and charts depicting the progress of the two vessels, to which spice was added because one ship was faster than the other. Even the fact that the *Laurentic* was bound to win failed to reduce the excitement. On arrival in the St Lawrence three police officers, one of whom was Inspector Dew, boarded the *Montrose* from a rowing boat, disguised as pilots.

Dew was able to identify Crippen as soon as he saw him and the guilty pair were placed under arrest. The British Government recognised that Captain Kendall's initiative had been responsible for bringing Crippen and his accomplice to justice, and he was presented with a cheque for £250 in recognition of the service he had rendered to the public.

Four years later, Captain Kendall again had occasion to appreciate the value of wireless telegraphy, when the vessel of which he was then commanding, the *Empress of Ireland*, was rammed in the St Lawrence by a Norwegian collier, and sank with a great loss of life, as is described in the following section in this chapter.

THE SINKING OF THE *EMPRESS OF IRELAND*

On 29th May 1914, a tragedy not far short of the *Titanic* occurred when the *Empress of Ireland*, owned by Canadian Pacific Railways, was in collision with the Norwegian collier *Storstad* near Father Point in the St Lawrence. There was thick fog at the time and in those days radar had not been invented. The bows of the *Storstad* impacted the *Empress of Ireland* amidships and full on, and it was clear from the moment of the impact that the vessel was doomed.

The Chief Radio Officer of the *Empress of Ireland*, Ronald Ferguson, immediately sent out a distress call, which was received by the Marconi Station at Father Point. The Canadian Government vessels *Eureka* and *Lady Evelyn*, which were in the vicinity, immediately made for the scene of the disaster to rescue survivors. The conditions were horrific, for the temperature of the water was only about four degrees above freezing. Of the 1,467

58. R.M.S. *Empress of Ireland.*
(Photograph: Collection of Edward C. Heukels)

souls aboard, only 444 survived, and they undoubtedly owed their lives to wireless telegraphy.

Ronald Ferguson's subsequent report, which is quoted below, is rivetting in its dramatic interest, and particularly so to the author who became closely acquainted with him in later years when Mr Ferguson became first the General Manager and then the Managing Director of the Marconi International Marine Communication Company Ltd.

The first intimation of anything having happened was when the whistle commenced blowing at approximately 1.45 a.m. Mr Bamford, the junior Radio Officer, had just relieved me ten minutes previously and when the vessel struck I came into the operating room and took over the 'phones' from him, instructing him to ask the bridge if we were to send out a distress signal. Between the time of the collision and the time the dynamos went out of commission we had only eight minutes. My cabin was on the top deck. Immediately after the shock, I saw lights passing as I ran to the wireless room where I called all stations with the message 'Stand by for distress signal have struck something'. The Chief Officer later said, 'Call SOS', so I sent out the message 'SOS, have struck something, sinking fast, send help'.

The station at Father Point, which had previously answered my preliminary call, replied immediately, asking where we were. I replied

67

'Twenty miles past Rimouski'. I was trying to confirm the answer at the request of Father Point when the power failed. Water had got into the stoke-hold, cut off the steam and put the generators out of commission. Before taking off the headphones I got from Father Point the message 'OK, sending *Eureka*, *Lady Evelyn* your assistance'. Mr Bamford, my junior, had in the meantime brought me some clothes, and when I had put them on I ran out along the deck from which many people were jumping into the icy water, and shouted, 'Plenty of assistance is coming, and a ship will be here in less than an hour'. I then returned to my cabin and was preparing to work the emergency gear when the ship gave a fearful lurch, causing the accumulators to burst open the doors of the cupboard and scatter their contents over the floor of the cabin. As it was impossible to do more, I went out on deck and picked up a deck-chair, and just as I had put my arm through it I was thrown into the water as the ship turned on her side and sank. When Mr Bamford was thrown out of the ship he landed safely in a floating boat.

After swimming for about quarter of an hour I managed to scramble into a lifeboat, from which I was able to reach the *Storstad*. When the *Lady Evelyn* came alongside I jumped aboard her and gained entry into her wireless cabin by means of the window.

As she had no wireless man, I used her gear to establish communication with Father Point Station, through which I communicated all details of the disaster of which I had knowledge in a message to the Marconi Company in London, after having asked for clothes and supplies and a train to be sent to Rimouski Wharf. When Mr Bamford reached the *Storstad* he took out one of her boats and rendered what assistance he could. He then boarded the *Eureka* with those whom he had rescued and these were landed at Rimouski. The bows of the *Storstad* are striking evidence of the force with which she struck the *Empress of Ireland.*

The first account of the incident received in London by the Marconi Transatlantic Service was that sent by Ronald Ferguson. Later, a fuller report was received from Mr W. J. Whiteside, the Officer in Charge at Father Point.

The Marconi Radio Officers in the *Empress of Ireland* gave evidence before the Commission of Enquiry held in Canada. One sentence spoken by Lord Mersey deserves recording as a testimony to their work: 'You spoke well, you young gentlemen, you are a credit to the service you are in.'

Mr Whiteside, at Father Point Station, was also warmly complimented for the prompt and effective measures he took to rush assistance to the doomed vessel. The chairman expressed his opinion that but for his presence of mind not one of those on board the *Empress of Ireland* would have lived to tell the tale.

Just two weeks after the *Empress of Ireland* sank, the House of Commons was debating the Mercantile Shipping Bill, which was intended to minimise the dangers of the sea. The compulsory wireless telegraphy clauses provided that every British ship which carried fifty or more persons should have a wireless installation and should maintain a wireless telegraph service sufficient to comply with the Act, and should carry certified operators or wireless watchers. However, the Act did not extend to vessels engaged on coastal voyages which did not take them more than 150 miles from the coast, and it did not apply to sailing ships.

As an interesting postscript to the fore-going, the author accompanied Ronald Ferguson, then General Manager of the Marconi International Marine Communication Company, to the International Radio Conference at Geneva in 1959. At the time she was (under a different name) attached to the United Kingdom Post Office Delegation to the conference, under the leadership of W. Billington, then UK Inspector of Wireless Telegraphy. The *Empress of Ireland* incident happened to crop up during a lunch-time conversation at which a member of the Canadian delegation was present, and from it later resulted, as an agreeable surprise to Ronald Ferguson, in a formal presentation, at which the author was present, to him of a duplicate of the 1st Class PMG Certificate he had lost when the *Empress of Ireland* sank.

59. White Star Line poster advertising the *Titanic*, c.1912.
(Photograph: Merseyside Maritime Museum)

CHAPTER 4

CQD MGY – The Wireless side of the 'Titanic' Disaster – Marconi at the New York Enquiry

RADIO OFFICERS PHILLIPS, BRIDE AND COTTAM

O N THE 20th OF APRIL 1912, the East Room in the Waldorf-Astoria Hotel in New York was filled to overflowing with spectators anxious to follow a US Senate hearing convened to investigate the *Titanic* disaster only four days previously. Among them was Guglielmo Marconi, who had been subpoenaed to attend the enquiry.

The entrance of Harold Bride, aged twenty-two, the junior and only surviving Radio Officer of the *Titanic*, being pushed into the room in a wheelchair with his left foot heavily bandaged created a minor sensation.

60. The only known photograph of the Radio Room in the *Titanic*, taken by Father Brown, who left the ship before its fatal voyage (showing Harold Bride working).
(Photograph: Father Brown and 'Titanic' Historical Society)

71

JUNE
1912

The MARCONIGRAPH

PAGE
103

Mr. J. Durrant, of the "Mount
Temple."

Mr. Gilbert W. Balfour,
Marconi Operator on board the "Baltic,"
who was on the same vessel when she went
to the rescue of the "Republic."

Mr. Cyril Evans, of the
"Californian."

Mr. H. T. Cottam, of the "Carpathia."

61. Radio Officers, *Titanic.*
(Photograph: Marconi plc)

The sinking of the *Titanic* on the evening of 14th April 1912, has generated so much literature that to expand it by a chapter in this book may seem out of place. But in fact the explosive combination of the new science of wireless telegraphy, high drama and allegations of cheque-book journalism involving Marconi himself, and triggered by the disaster burst upon the world media like a volcanic explosion.

The arrest of Dr Crippen in July 1912 on the Canadian Pacific Liner *Montrose* as a result of a wireless message had attracted world-wide publicity at the time, but that was nothing compared to the journalistic frenzy created by the *Titanic* disaster. And there, in the ornate East Room of the Waldorf-Astoria, was presented to the public a dramatic example of the then still unfamiliar world of wireless communication.

The Senate hearing had been rushed into existence notwithstanding the fact that the *Titanic* was a British registered vessel with British Officers, and had sunk in international waters. The US Attorney General had ruled that because the vessel was actually owned by an American Trust (basically J. P. Morgan) jurisdiction existed for a Congressional investigation with the right to subpoena British subjects to testify before it.

On the British side of the Atlantic this action was regarded as high-handed, and it aroused a great deal of ire, notably from Joseph Conrad on what he described as 'these Bumble-like proceedings'. In an article printed in the *English Review* in the month following the disaster, he asked why should an officer in the British Merchant Service answer questions from any 'king, emperor, autocrat, or senator of any foreign power as to an event in which a British ship alone was concerned, and which did not even take place in the territorial waters of that place'. It passed his understanding, and he went on to say 'and what did they find out? Only that a ship scraped her side along a piece of ice, and sank after floating for two and a half hours, taking a lot of people with her. If there was any lesson to be learned, it was the tragedy of the fatuous drowning of all those people who to the last moment put their trust in mere bigness, in the reckless affirmations of commercial men and mere technicians, and in the irresponsible paragraphs of the newspapers booming these ships!'

Before Harold Bride was asked to speak, Radio Officer Harold Thomas Cottam, sole operator on the Cunard Liner *Carpathia*, which rescued the survivors of the *Titanic*, transfixed the hearing with a mixture of drama and the workings of Fate. At 12.15 a.m. on Sunday, 14th April, Cottam had been on continuous duty since 7 a.m. and was getting undressed as he prepared to go to bed. His instruments were still switched on because he was waiting

62. Radio Officer Harold
Thomas Cottam, *Carpathian*.
(Photograph: Marconi plc)

63. 2nd Radio Officer Harold Bride
of the *Titanic*, who was trained at the
British School of Telegraphy Ltd.
(Photograph: David Evans)

for one last message, a confirmation of an earlier one that he had sent to the Allan Liner *Parisian*. Except for this he would have shut down his station, and there might have been no survivors from the *Titanic*.

Hoping to kill a few minutes, he decided to call the *Titanic*, which he knew was in the vicinity, and listened on the appropriate frequency. The *Titanic* seemed busy with wireless traffic, but finding a break, Cottam broke in with, 'I say, old man, do you know there is a batch of messages coming through for you at MCC (Cape Cod)?' Stunned, Cottam heard Jack Phillips, the senior Radio Officer on the *Titanic* respond by transmitting the distress call CQD.

The rest is well-known; the *Carpathia* was only about fifty-eight miles south-east of the *Titanic*, and her Master, Captain Arthur Rostron, earned fame and universal gratitude for organising the rescue in a manner that has to be described as a textbook example of planning and foresight.

The Senate committee had elected one of their number, Senator William Alden Smith, aged fifty-three, of Michigan, as Chairman, and in this capacity he relentlessly interrogated one witness after another. His manner was abrupt, and if nothing else he achieved a reputation for objective questioning. An attorney, and member of the board of a company operating Lake Michigan steamships, Smith possessed all the qualifications to head the enquiry.

Harold Bride's testimony concentrated attention still further on the part played in the disaster by wireless telegraphy. The court was electrified when,

64. Radio Officer John (Jack) Phillips of the *Titanic*.
(Photograph: Marconi plc)

in answer to a question by Senator Smith, Bride told the hearing that a message had been received from the Leyland Line Steamer *Californian*, giving the position of three large icebergs it had just passed to Captain Smith of the *Titanic*.

When the collision occurred Bride was asleep in the operator's cabin which adjourned the Radio Office, but woke up shortly afterwards, although it was not the collision that had awakened him.

He dressed and joined the senior Radio Officer, Jack Phillips, in the Radio Office, where Phillips said: 'She had just got damaged in some way, and that he expected we should have to return to Harland and Wolffs for repairs.' Phillips had just received a large batch of messages from Cape Race and was in the act of handing over the watch to Bride when Captain Smith entered the room and told Phillips, 'You had better get assistance.' Whereupon Phillips sent out the distress call CQD MGY (MGY was the call sign of the *Titanic*) half a dozen times.

At that point Guglielmo Marconi was called as a witness and asked by Senator Smith and others to explain what CQ and CQD meant.

> Marconi: 'It is a conventional signal.'
> Mr Uhler: 'Is it an arbitrary signal?'

75

Marconi: 'It is arbitrary, but it is conventional. Everybody understands it. CQ means "All stations", does it not, Mr Bride?'

Bride: 'Yes, sir.'

Marconi: 'CQ is the call for all stations. If you call CQ on a ship it means "All other stations stand at attention and reply". I did not make the signals originally. I presume the object was to indicate, in a certain way, to all stations, the danger . . . that existed.'

Mr Kirlin: 'Or distress?'

Marconi: 'Or distress, yes. I should add that the danger signal, introduced or decided on by the Berlin Convention, is SOS.'

Senator Smith: 'What does that mean?'

Marconi: 'I do not know what it means. It denotes danger or distress. I believe that was sent, too, from the *Titanic*; but of course Mr Bride will tell you if it is a fact.'

Senator Smith: 'What is the silent signal?'

Marconi: 'I do not know it, personally.'

Senator Smith: 'Under the international convention, I mean.'

Bride: 'It is DDD.'

Marconi: 'DDD.'

Senator Smith: 'That is the silent signal?'

Marconi: 'Yes, sir; that means "shut up".'

Senator Smith: 'All other stations must cease?'

Marconi: 'All other stations must cease.'

Senator Smith: 'But the danger signal CQD is the recognised signal for a ship in distress?'

Marconi: 'Yes.'

Senator Smith: 'You received a reply within three or four minutes, but you only know from what . . .'

Bride: 'Mr Phillips told me.'

Senator Smith: 'Just what did he tell you?'

Bride: 'He told me to go to the Captain and report the *Frankfurt*.'

Senator Smith: 'What do you mean by the *Frankfurt*?'

Bride: 'He was in communication with the *Frankfurt*, sir; he had sent the *Frankfurt* our position.'

Senator Smith: 'Was the *Frankfurt* the first ship that picked up the CQD?'

Bride: 'Yes, sir.'

The first ship to acknowledge the *Titanic*'s CQD was the German steamer *Frankfurt*, owned by North German Lloyd. According to Bride, Phillips had assumed that the operator on the *Frankfurt* would have informed his Captain, but apparently he did not. Instead, he sent another message to the *Titanic* enquiring, 'What was the matter?', to which Phillips replied, 'You are a fool; just stand by.' At this point Marconi was again addressed by Senator Smith.

Senator Smith: 'Mr Marconi, do you know how the *Frankfurt* is equipped?'

Marconi: 'The *Frankfurt* is, I believe, a ship belonging to the North German Lloyd. She is equipped by a German company, called DEBEG Co. It means a lot of things in German, each letter, which I will not go into, of which I am a director.'

Senator Smith: 'You are a director in the German company?'

Marconi: 'Yes.'

Senator Smith: 'You are familiar with the wireless equipment or apparatus?'

Marconi: 'I am not familiar with the wireless equipment on that particular ship.'

Senator Smith: 'So you would be unable to make a comparative statement – to make comparison between the equipment or apparatus on the *Carpathia* and the *Frankfurt*?'

Marconi: 'I would be unable, sir, to do it.'

Senator Smith: 'Would the fact that the *Frankfurt* is equipped with apparatus of a German type in any way lessen their interest in calls made through the Marconi machine or apparatus?'

Marconi: 'No; because it is Marconi apparatus. It is made in Germany, but it is made under my patents under an arrangement we have with German interests.'

Senator Smith: 'Let me ask you: Are the regulations of Germany, with reference to the operation and use of wireless telegraphy, in perfect harmony with the Berlin Convention?'

Marconi: 'Absolutely. They were enacted at Berlin and most of them were inspired by the German Government.'

Senator Smith: 'Are these calls that are recognised prescribed in the Berlin Convention?'

Marconi: 'The call of the Berlin Convention, which has only recently been introduced, is this SOS call, but the Marconi companies have used and use the CQD call. The *Frankfurt*, which was equipped with wireless, belonging to one of I may call the Marconi companies because I would not be a director of the company if it was not associated with us.'

Senator Smith: 'Do you think that any confusion would arise, growing out of this international arrangement of the signal, with the Marconi signal?'

Marconi: 'No. I should state that the international signal is really less known than the Marconi Co's signal.'

Senator Smith: 'So that the CQD call must have been understood with its full significance by the *Frankfurt* operator?'

Marconi: 'I have absolutely no doubt of that.'

After still more questions by Senator Smith, which to many seemed to be hammering away at the obvious, Bride then described the circumstances of his leaving the *Titanic*. At Phillips's request, Bride gathered up his spare money, put on another coat, and prepared to leave the ship. He then went on to describe how he got into a collapsible lifeboat on the boat-deck, which was then washed overboard by a wave and ended up floating upside down with Bride and others inside it.

There was breathing space within the boat and eventually he managed to free himself, and after swimming around for a while returned to it and, with others, clung to the upturned bottom until he was picked up. Phillips, who had entered the boat with him, was not so lucky, and died under the upturned boat.

One of the surviving passengers was Joseph Bruce Ismay, the Managing Director of the White Star Line, and son of its founder, Thomas Ismay. Ismay was the subject of much adverse criticism, particularly in America, for having entered a lifeboat while women and children remained on the *Titanic*. It was somehow felt that, like Captain Smith, he should have been standing on the bridge when the ship went down. His explanation, that he only stepped into the lifeboat, which was almost level with the deck, after all the women and children within sight had got into the boat, was greeted with disbelief. The affair clouded the rest of his life, although he was exonerated at the enquiry conducted by the British Board of Trade under the chairmanship of the Wreck Commissioner, whose comment was that if Ismay had not stepped into the boat at the time, it would only have added another name to the list of lives lost.

Of much more concern were the charges resulting from wireless tele-graphy messages he sent from the *Carpathia* after his rescue. It was alleged that as soon as Ismay learned that the US Senate had set up an enquiry, and were subpoenaing witnesses, he set in motion urgent plans to avoid having to give evidence himself, and sent the following message to Philip

A. S. Franklin, Vice-President of the American company International Mercantile Marine, which actually owned the White Star Line:

> Most desirable *Titanic* crew aboard *Carpathia* should be returned home earliest moment possible. Suggest you hold *Cedric*, sailing her daylight Friday unless you see any reason contrary. Propose returning in her myself. Please send outfit of clothes, for me to *Cedric*. Have nothing of my own. Please reply.
>
> Yamsi (Ismay's telegraphic name)

> To Ismay, *Carpathia*: Have arranged forward crew *Lapland* sailing Saturday, calling Plymouth. We all consider most unwise delay *Cedric*.
>
> Franklin

> To Franklin: Very important you should hold *Cedric* daylight for *Titanic* crew. Reply.
>
> Yamsi

After several exchanges along these lines, Franklin finally sent the following:

> Ismay, *Carpathia*: Regret after fullest consideration decided *Cedric* must sail as scheduled. Expect join *Carpathia* at quarantine, but do not remove boats, as everything arranged for steamer, proceed docks immediately.
>
> Franklin

In the end, the US Senate made it clear that when the *Carpathia* arrived at the quarantine station all survivors whose testimony was required at the hearing would be subpoenaed to appear before it.

On the sixth day of the hearing, those present were able to enjoy a touch of scandal when Marconi, to whose invention the survivors owed their lives, was grilled by Senator Smith over his alleged role in what was described at the time as 'cheque-book journalism'. The allegation was that from the moment that Marconi first heard of the disaster he endeavoured as far as possible to monitor and control any statements that might be made by Radio Officers Bride and Cottam. Both were employees of the company which bore his name, and as such were bound by the conditions of their employment, and no doubt by a sense of their own interest, to safeguard their employer's interests. An alleged can of worms was opened up when

Senator Smith read out a communication that had been sent by the commanding officer of the US naval vessel *Florida* to the Secretary of the Navy:

On the evening of the steamship *Carpathia*'s arrival in New York, the following four radiograms were intercepted by the chief operator, J. R. Simpson, chief electrician, United States Navy. They appear to me to be significant enough to be brought to the attention of the department.

Seagate to *Carpathia* – 8.12 p.m.: Sat, old man, Marconi Co taking good care of you. Keep your mouth shut, and hold your story. It is fixed so that you will get big money. Now please do your best to clear.

Next – To Marconi Officer *Carpathia* and *Titanic*: Arranged for your exclusive story for dollars in four figures. Mr Marconi agreeing. Say nothing until you see me. Where are you now? J. M. Sammis (General Engineer, Marconi Wireless Telegraph Company of America).

Next – From *Seagate* to *Carpathia* operator: Go to Strand Hotel, 502 West Fourteenth Street. To meet Mr Marconi.

And – *Seagate* to *Carpathia*: A personal to operator *Carpathia*. Meet Mr Marconi and Sammis at Strand Hotel, 502 West Fourteenth Street. Keep your mouth shut.

Senator Smith to Marconi: 'What can you say about that, Mr Marconi?'

Marconi: 'I do not know anything whatever about any of those messages. They are not in the phraseology which I would have approved of if I had passed them. I should, however, say that I told Mr Sammis or Mr Bottomley – I do not remember which – that I, as an officer of the British company would not prohibit or prevent these operators from making anything which they reasonably could out of selling their story of the wreck. I was anxious that, if possible, they might make some small amount of money out of the information they had.'

Senator Smith: 'Is that the custom of your company?'

Marconi: 'It is not a custom; it is a thing that is done . . .'

Senator Smith: 'Is it a habit?'

Marconi: 'No, it is not a habit. It is done on very special occasions . . .'

Senator Smith: 'Mr Marconi, do you wish the committee to understand that you approve that method?'

Marconi: 'I was in favour of it, or at least I approved of or consented to his getting something out of it.'

Senator Smith: 'I know, but let me ask you this. With the right to exact compensation for an exclusive story detailing the horrors of the greatest sea disaster that ever occurred in the history of the world, do you mean that an operator under your company's direction shall have the right to prevent the public from knowing of that calamity . . .'

Marconi (interrupting): 'No.'

Senator Smith (continuing): 'Hold on a moment. From knowing of that calamity except through the exclusive appropriation of the facts by the operator who is cognisant of them?'

Marconi: 'I say, not at all. I gave no instructions in regard to withholding any information, and I gave no advice or instructions in regard to any exclusive story to anybody. The only thing I did say or authorise was that if he were offered payment for a story of the disaster, he was permitted, so far as the English company went, to take that money.'

Senator Smith: 'You have seen the rumours of this matter, have you not, in the papers?'

Marconi: 'Yes.'

Senator Smith: 'I have not seen those rumours; but after seeing those rumours did you talk with Sammis about the matter?'

Marconi: 'I saw Mr Sammis for a few moments some time ago, and I told him – I said, "You know I did not authorise that message".'

Senator Smith: 'When did you tell him that?'

Marconi: 'I told him that since the survivors were landed. I do not remember the exact date.'

Senator Smith: 'About what time?'

Marconi: 'Three or four days ago, I should say.'

Senator Smith: 'Have you talked with him about it since?'

Marconi: No, sir. I should like to state in explanation, also, of this matter . . .'

Senator Smith: 'Please do; I would like to have you, in your own way. I am not seeking to embarrass you at all. I simply felt it was my duty to get the information I asked for.'

Marconi: 'What I meant and intended when I stated to the operator that he could take something for a story or for an account of the disaster was that newspapers and reporters would be so interested in what he had to say, and in himself personally, in view of the fact especially that Bride had behaved in such a brave and gallant manner, that, without withholding any general information, they would be ready to pay him an amount for a story or description which he could give them.'

Senator Smith: 'Have you finished?'

Marconi: 'Yes, sir.'

Senator Smith: 'Mr Marconi, did you expect the operator to syndicate this information, or give it exclusively to one newspaper?'

Marconi: 'I did not expect him to give it exclusively.'

Senator Smith: 'Did you expect him to put it up to the highest bidder?'

Marconi: 'No, sir.'

Senator Smith: 'If I understand you correctly, you did not seek to control the operator, at all, in what he would say, or to whom he would say it?'

Marconi: 'No, I did not.'

Senator Smith: 'Do you know what use of the words "Arranged for your exclusive story for dollars in four figures, Mr Marconi agreeing. Say nothing until you see me. J. M. Sammis" would indicate? What did he mean by four figures?'

Marconi: 'I suppose it was something over a thousand dollars; but if you will allow me to repeat again . . .'

Senator Smith: 'Please do. I wish you to say anything you want about it.'

Marconi (continuing): 'For the fourth or fifth or sixth time, I say that I know nothing whatever about those messages.'

Senator Smith: 'And you understand I am not saying that you do.'

Marconi: 'Thank you.'

Senator Smith: 'I am simply enquiring. Do you know whether Cottam or Bride sold their story?'

Marconi: 'I think they received remuneration for it, and that may be called "sold", I presume. I mean that they were paid for it.'

Senator Smith: 'Do you know how much they got?'

Marconi: 'I do not know how much Cottam got.'

Senator Smith: 'Do you know how much Bride got?'

Marconi: 'I was told that Bride got $500.'

Senator Smith: 'From whom?'

Marconi: 'From the *New York Times*.'

Senator Smith: 'Who told you that?'

Marconi: 'I think it was Mr Bottomley.'

Senator Smith: 'The general manager of your company?'

Marconi: 'Yes. I should also say, I believe, one of the editors of the *New York Times*, either Mr Ochs or Van Ander.'

Senator Smith: 'Is any officer of the Marconi Co. interested in the *New York Times*?'

Marconi: 'I do not know. I do not think so, because if anyone was I would probably hear of it in some way.'

Senator Smith: 'Is any director of your company interested in the *New York Times*?'

Marconi: 'No.'

On the ninth day, Senator Smith continued his questioning, going over the same ground with Frederick Sammis, who defended his company vigorously.

Senator Smith: 'Let us clear up this matter as we go along. I think it is a most distasteful matter to you, as it is to the committee, and I think, the public.'

Sammis: 'I have not done anything I am ashamed of, and if I can clear my record, that the newspapers have impugned, I want to do it, and I am sure you want to help me.'

Senator Smith: 'Have you done anything in this matter, that you are very proud of?'

Sammis: 'I have not done anything I am ashamed of.'

Senator Smith: 'I did not ask you that. I want to know whether you are proud of it?'

Sammis: 'Yes; I am proud of the fact that, being an employer of labour, and being the superior of poorly paid men – men who do not see very much of this world's goods – I will do them a good turn honestly if I can, and that I consider I have done. I know of no law that can forbid a man selling his personal experience, after he comes ashore, and we have no rule by which we could prevent them from doing it.'

After more of the same Senator Smith hammered away yet again:

'You have spoken of rewarding the services of these operators. Mr Bride is here, and at the risk of saying something that I am not called upon to say, I want to observe that Mr Bride was so loyal to the *Titanic* and so obedient to its commander and so courageous in its distress, that he refused to leave the *Titanic* in a lifeboat, and stayed on the ship until one minute before she sank, because the captain had not given him permission to leave; and he remained at his apparatus all that time ticking off the fate of the ship. I want to know whether it would not be more creditable to you and your company to encourage that kind of gallantry and heroism and fidelity by leaving the question of reward to the public, rather than to seal his lips with an injunction of secrecy, so that he might receive a pittance from some private source?

Sammis: 'We did not seal his lips. We provided the means for unsealing them.'

Senator Smith: 'Did you not tell him to shut his mouth?'

Sammis: 'I did not.'

Note by the author: The above extracts are from the lengthy verbatim record of the US Senate Hearing as recorded in Senate Document No. 736 (issued by the Government Printing Office, Washington, 1913). Because so much controversy has surrounded the subject, it is owed to the memory of Marconi, Phillips, Bride and Cottam to ensure that the details are recorded as clearly as possible.

Radio Officer John George Phillips was born in Godalming in 1888 and began his career as a telegraph learner at Godalming Post Office. In March 1906 he joined the Marconi School at Liverpool, and went to sea in August 1906. He served on the *Teutonic, Pretorian, Buccaneer* and *Oceanic*, and between May 1908 and July 1911 was the operating staff of the high power transatlantic wireless station at Clifden.

Radio Officer Harold Thomas Cottam, born Nottinghamshire, 27th November, 1891, and trained at the British School of Telegraphy, South London, qualifying at the age of seventeen in 1908. His first appointment at sea was as a 2nd Radio Officer on the *Empress of Ireland*. At the age of twenty-one he was the sole Radio Officer on the *Carpathia*. He was presented by the Liverpool Shipwreck & Humane Society with a silver medal and an illuminated address for 'Praiseworthy and humane service to the survivors of the *Titanic*'. He died in 1984 at the age of ninety-three.

Harold Stanley Bride. Born 11th January 1890, in Hull. He attended the British School of Wireless Telegraphy, qualifying in July 1911 and, in 1912, was appointed by the Marconi Marine Company as junior Radio Officer on the *Titanic*. Between 1914-18 he served on the *Mona's Isle*. By 1923 he had resigned and moved to Scotland where he became a travelling salesman. He died in 1956.

CHAPTER 5

Conditions at Sea – The Radio Officer's Union and the Great Strike

THE FIRST RADIO OFFICERS AT SEA encountered a variety of reactions to their presence on board by ship's masters and their officers. Some were downright hostile; a ship's captain who had been at sea for twenty or more years without wireless telegraphy would frequently be resentful of 'carrying a passenger', merely 'to send or receive a few messages'. Even the contribution made by Radio Officers in times of emergency, sometimes at the cost of their lives, failed to penetrate their understanding, and the same applied to some shipowners. It was only when such characters themselves experienced a situation from which they could only be extracted by a Radio Officer that their attitude changed.

In some ways, the situation of the early Radio Officer was not unlike that of the first ship's engineers when steam engines began to be fitted on sailing ships. But Radio Officers were more vulnerable. An engineer would have served a long apprenticeship followed by at least several years experience ashore before going to sea; he would be more mature than a young Radio Officer in his teens or early twenties, whose training had at the most taken a year in a subject seemingly unrelated to ships.

Early Radio Officers and their equipment found themselves squeezed into tiny cabins, often with only just room to accommodate a chair. It was a tradition that began in 1901 with the first British ship to be fitted with wireless telegraphy equipment, the Beaver Line liner *Lake Champlain*. Because no accommodation was available, a special wooden cabin was constructed of match-boarding, with one side made up of a steel bulkhead. It was scarcely more than a cupboard, being 4'6" by 3'6" and completely without natural light – that commodity had to be made available by opening the door to the elements. The entire structure only cost £5.

The equipment was mounted on a green-baize covered table top, with accumulator batteries on the floor beneath it, and a charging board screwed

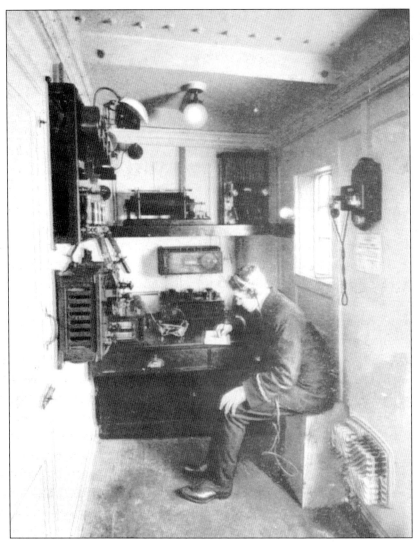

65. Radio room, c.1912 (believed to be on the Cunard passenger liner, *Carpathia*.
(Photograph: Marconi plc)

to the bulkhead. The apparatus included two large induction coils, which had arrived on board in boxes. One coil was a spare, and the two boxes were placed on top of each other to act as a seat, the empty one serving as a convenient cupboard for spares and other odds and ends.

In an article in the *Wireless World* in June 1917 (which developed from the Marconi Company's house magazine, *The Marconigraph*), the Radio Officer, F. S. Stacey, described the extraordinary interest his equipment aroused (see Appendix 2).

The *Lake Champlain* sailed on 21st May 1901, from Liverpool, bound for Halifax with about 1,200 people on board. Soon after sailing, numerous messages were exchanged with the stations at Holyhead and, later, Rosslare. But after that there was nothing for the Radio Officer to do, because there were no radio stations on the American side for him to contact. During the voyage to Halifax the passengers and crew were fascinated by the occult contents of his tiny cabin, which was continuously visited by curious sightseers. On arrival in port there was a similar interest, and when the ship got to Montreal she was visited by representatives from various scientific bodies.

Things took a long time to improve, as the experience of Radio Officer, V. A. K. Smith, which he related in the *Signal* (the monthly journal of the Radio Officer's Union) of June 1924 graphically illustrates. His vessel – unfortunately, the article does not does not give its name – sailed from Bahia Blanca on 31st March 1924. In the early hours of the following morning the ship was caught in a severe storm which soon reached hurricane force. A tremendous sea broke over the forecastle and stove in the number one hatch, and the ship had to be stopped while efforts were made to repair the hatch to prevent the hold from being flooded.

The radio room and Radio Officer's sleeping accommodation were combined in a wooden construction built on to an iron girder arrangement that overlapped the after well-deck – one of the most exposed positions on the ship. After coming off a two hour watch, Radio Officer Smith went into his sleeping quarters, where he wedged himself between a chest of drawers and his bunk. Suddenly, there was a terrific crash and he was plunged into darkness. At the same time the whole wooden structure was washed overboard, and he found himself under water and entangled in wreckage. Somehow he managed to crawl out, struggling to swim in mountainous seas. The wreckage of the wireless cabin was floating and he clung to it, hoping that he would be rescued by the crew of the ship, which the Master was manoeuvring nearer to him.

Eventually, a life-buoy was flung near him, which he succeeded in grabbing. The ship was rolling and plunging heavily and he was frightened the poop would come crashing down on top of him. Then suddenly he felt himself being heaved out of the water and pulled on board, having missed drowning by the narrowest of margins.

It would be nice to report that this incident would have caused the Board of Trade to introduce regulations. However, thirteen years later, things were still not much better, as the following extract from the *Signal* of August 1937 reveals:

87

The Wireless Room was situated on the starboard side, forward of the amidship house on the main deck, with outside door, bulwark abreast and rails on the foredeck. On opening this door in a gale, it was torn out of my grip and smashed against the iron bulkhead, the panelling of this solid teak door was badly broken, and bent outwards, and despite immediate efforts at lashing from the inside, was finally torn off its hinges and carried halfway up the foredeck. The wireless room was partially flooded by driving rain and salt spray (being light ship) which rendered the receiver temporarily useless and transmission very poor due to weakening of the insulation. Within the hour we went into Distress, and thanks to the Auto-Alarm, reception of the answering calls was made possible, but I feel confident that under the same circumstances there would have been no response had the vessel been loaded and at a greater distance from the nearest station.

The vessel in question is nearing the end of her long service, but the fact remains that any position or structure for Wireless Rooms meets with B.O.T. approval. They may be boxes bolted on the after end of boat-decks, where strong lifeboats are commonly smashed and lost over the side. The operator may live at the greatest possible distance from his apparatus . . . is the prospective life-saver to risk certain accident or a possibility of being swept over the side in attempting to reach the Wireless Room in one minute, or should he dress, don sea-boots, study which is the safest alleyway, proceed with caution against the elements, switch off and tune in, etc. . . . in time to avert disaster?

In March 1923, at the annual banquet of the Chamber of Shipping of the United Kingdom, at the Savoy Hotel in London, Mr Richard Holt, a well-known Liverpool shipowner, responded to the toast with a severe attack on the necessity being placed upon shipowners to carry Radio Officers as follows:

He would like to see a full enquiry into the question of wireless at sea. People would be appalled at the cost of wireless to shipowners set up in the hope of saving life at sea. The only result was that they were increasing the cost of living, and instead of saving life making it more difficult to live. That was certainly the result of putting three able-bodied young men on board a ship for a message that never came. From the economic point of view all these young gentlemen might just as well be dead. He would like to see that those gentlemen who asked others to come and help them with S.O.S. signals be made to pay for those signals.

It is not often that the author finds herself at a loss for words; some in fact do occur to her, but unfortunately they are not suitable for publication.

The Second World War heralded a change; it could hardly do otherwise. The Merchant Service was re-christened the 'Merchant Navy' and all ships came under the control of the Ministry of War Transport. Shipowners were then not engaged in looking for commercially profitable freights and were guaranteed a reasonable if not generous return on the capital invested in their ships. And if any ships were sunk by enemy action they were compensated accordingly. Indeed, one well-known shipowner was convicted and jailed for claiming for ships that were not lost at all; as an act of clemency he was allowed out of jail to die at home. But after the war conditions improved enormously in pay and accommodation for all seafarers, and steadily grew better, with recreation rooms and even separate cabins for the crew. Sadly, this improvement only came as the British Merchant fleet declined drastically in numbers and the years of British supremacy upon the seas of the world came to an end.

CONDITIONS OF SERVICE

The author has in her possession a copy of an intimidating volume issued by the Marconi Marine Company in 1912 entitled 'General Orders'. Interestingly, it covers both the ship and land stations operated by the company. This book was the Radio Officer's 'Bible' and it had to be more or less committed to memory, less dire consequences ensued. Reading it, one is reminded of the absolute obedience then demanded by employers, in work, and often out of it. For instance, Rule 6 – Staff Records:

> At the Head Office of the Company a staff record of every operator in the service is kept, in which all particulars regarding the general conduct and manner in which telegraphic and clerical duties have been carried out, are recorded; special attention being given to the observance or non-observance of the Company's Regulations.

And Rule 7:

The remarks and entries made in each staff record are taken into full account when the annual increments are under consideration.

Again, Rule 12:

Telegraphists should remember that they are not in any way entitled to leave of absence as a right, but that it is a privilege which may be earned by attention to duty and general good work. Generally, 14 days leave of absence, per annum, will be granted to each operator.

Rule 15b:

Operators on board ship shall always wear the regulation uniform approved by the Company while on board ship; it is similar to the undress uniform worn by officers of the Merchant Marine and consists of: Blue Uniform. Reefer coat; double-breasted (dark navy blue serge or cloth; eight buttons, Marconi type.) Trousers: same material as coat. Boots: Black. Collar: White linen and black tie. Cap (Regulation pattern, as worn by officers) and Marconi badge.

On certain lines the senior operator wears a double gold braided band on the sleeves of the coat; junior operator a single gold band.

White Uniform. Tunic: single breasted (white duck or drill), black cloth epaulets with letter M in gold. Trousers: same material as tunic. Cap: ordinary blue cap with white cap cover.

On ships of the White Star Line operators do not wear the gold braid on uniform.

The book next lays down the Radio Officer's responsibilities in the care of the equipment in his charge, and also his watch-keeping duties. It then goes on to specify in excruciating detail everything to do with the clerical and accounting duties relating to wireless telegraph traffic, down to the last halfpenny.

Rule 38. Watch-Keeping Duties:
The instruments shall not be left unattended during working hours. At all stations provided with two or more operators a continuous watch is insisted upon. Any breach of this regulation will be regarded seriously.

On ships carrying one operator, he will arrange to be on duty at such hours as are necessary to establish communication at the earliest possible moment with shore stations, and with ships listed on the Communication Charts, and it is necessary that the commander be aware of the periods during which the operator is off duty taking rest. Therefore, telegraphists serving on single-handed ships shall notify the commander or officer-on-watch of their times of going on and off duty.

In order to facilitate the establishment of communication between one man ships at sea, until midnight, 30th June 1913, operators when not taking rest shall call 'CQ' (All ships), and listen in for thirty minutes (GMT to be strictly observed) in accordance with the following table . . .

As an interesting interlude to this rather dull information, included by the author for completeness rather than interest, Rule 43 provides some light relief:

Should it be brought to the Company's notice that any operator has been guilty of using profane or abusive language in connection with his duties, he will be INSTANTLY DISMISSED.

The wireless accounts and supporting telegram forms had to be dispatched at the end of each voyage, or at three monthly intervals if the ship was on an extended voyage, to the Accounts Department at Head Office, where they were scrutinised in detail by clerks who themselves operated under the eagle eye of a supervisor, lest a halfpenny undercharged was overlooked. In that case the heavens opened up on the unfortunate Radio Officer concerned, who would receive a stinging letter of rebuke, stating that the sum in question would be deducted from his salary, and an adverse note made in his Staff Record of this grave dereliction of duty. Over-charging, where the Radio Officer had inadvertently collected an excess amount, did not usually attract a letter.

The author knows from personal experience that this procedure still operated in the late 1940s, though the limit might have been increased to one penny, and recalls with enormous satisfaction how in 1961, when as Personnel and Operating Manager of the Marconi Marine Company, having the opportunity of doing something about it.

The later 'General Orders' then in force, of course much expanded from its early predecessor, was still written in the same vein. Moreover, as was intimated by her predecessor, who joined the company in 1909, it was considered not a bad thing for the regulations to be written in as complicated a manner as possible, because whatever then happened, Head Office could interpret it in such a manner as to blame the Radio Officer. One of the first and most satisfying tasks on assuming control of the sea staff and traffic accounting was to sit down and re-write the whole book in a shortened, simplified and unambiguous manner.

A humorous example of a surviving anachronism from the same stable was the company's medical form for new Radio Officer entrants. Under 'Directions to Company Medical Officers', which had been unchanged since 1910, it stated, under the heading 'Applicant's Height': 'To be measured without hat or boots'.

In the early days of wireless fittings on ships in the Merchant Navy, the Marconi Company enjoyed a virtual monopoly, supplying both the equipment and the Radio Officer to operate it under system of rental/maintenance charges. But by the early 20s this situation changed as some shipowners began to employ their own Radio Officers, and other manufacturers of marine radio equipment offered competitive equipment. Other radio companies started up, such as the Radio Communication Company, the brain child of Ronald Ferguson, an ex-Marconi Radio Officer (see page 66), who later became the Managing Director of the Marconi Marine Company. It was not long before RCC began to take such a large slice of Marconi business that it was bought out by them and incorporated as one unit under the name of the British Wireless Marine Service.

In the 1930s another company, The International Marine Radio Company, offered a similar service of supplying equipment, the Radio Officers to operate it, and handling the telegraph traffic settlements with the British General Post Office and equivalent foreign authorities. IMRC received a tremendous boost in the mid-30s when they secured the contract for the *Queen Mary*, then the wonder of the age.

The charge for a radio-telegram was made up of three parts: a Ship Station Charge, Coast Station Charge and a Landline Charge. It was the usual practice when a shipping company employed a radio company to share the ship charge equally between them. In the case of the *Queen Mary*, where the volume of traffic was bound to be enormous, substantial sums of money were at stake. The author was told by a reliable informant that the Marconi Company lost the order because, under the mistaken impression that it enjoyed a virtual monopoly, it demanded an excessive share of the ship charge. It cost the company dear, for the publicity value of the *Queen*

Mary was huge, and IMRC benefited from it for years. They never employed Radio Officers in numbers which approached the Marconi Marine Company, although they remained in business until the end of of the Radio Officer era.

Another radio company, of similarly high standing, was Siemens (later known as AEI), based in Woolwich. It was bought out by Marconi Marine in the late 1960s, who took over the sea staff and equipment on ships.

Redifon, based in south London, was another company which supplied Radio Officers and equipment to Deep-Sea Ships, and was also well established in Hull, where it offered a service for Deep-Sea Trawlers

These radio companies employed Radio Officers in much fewer numbers than Marconi Marine, and enjoyed a very high reputation for their treatment of the Radio Officers in their service. To some extent this must have been made easier by the smaller numbers employed; each Radio Officer could be more individually known to those in the company who dealt with them.

By that time, more and more shipping companies were employing their own Radio Officers directly, although this was a trend that had begun many years before, with major shipping companies like Alfred Holts, The New Zealand Shipping Company, followed later by P&O, BP Tankers, and others.

Vessels operated by the Royal Fleet Auxiliary, mainly supply ships and tankers, occupied a position, so to speak, somewhere between the Merchant Navy and the Royal Navy. Radio Officers on these ships usually possessed the standard Merchant Navy qualifications – PMG Certificate, MOT Radar Maintenance Certificate, etc. – but were directly employed, paid, and administered by a special department of the Royal Navy.

A considerable number of Radio Officers commenced their careers with Marconi Marine, and then left after gaining their sea-time for higher paid employment with such shipowners. The radio companies could do little about it, for their salary scales were tied to the National Maritime Board Scales. As more of their Radio Officers left, the radio companies found themselves increasingly short of men and, therefore, had to restrict granting leave if ships were not to be held up. Inevitably, Radio Officers understandably left the radio companies for more money and more pay, so the situation grew steadily worse. And it was compounded by the often very high wages paid by the owners of foreign flag ships, particularly those of Greek registry.

The salary scales for Radio Officers, as for other seafarers, were largely decided by the National Maritime Board, a body consisting of the employers

– Shipowners and Radio Companies – and the various seafaring Unions. The protracted deliberations of this assembly, of which the author was for some years a member, resembled a sort of annual ritual in which all the parties indulged in a stately dance. In fact, it was all more or less agreed beforehand, so to speak, in a smoke-filled room, which led to a much easier life for all concerned. Occasionally, there was a blow-up when someone departed from the script, but usually the Chairman, Sir Richard Snedden, sorted this out fairly quickly – at least while he was still alive; sadly, he was killed when his son hit him over the head from behind.

The wage scales for Radio Officers were about as complicated as the human mind could conceive, ranging from low rates at the bottom to very good ones after many years at sea. They were enshrined in a document entitled 'The National Maritime Yearbook', remembered with distaste by anybody who had anything to do with it. It was a kind of industrial 'Bible', filled with torturous clauses relating to leave, conditions of service, travelling expenses and all sorts of allowances. After each set of negotiations a fresh wave of amendment slips had to be pasted in, expanding the book to unwieldy proportions, and referring backwards and forwards to various clauses until a Philadelphia lawyer was really required to unravel it, and a degree in Pelmanism.

Radio Officers, like other members of the crew, were paid on a voyage basis, which provided another nice little earner for the Marconi Company. Monthly allotments could be paid to dependants, but some money had to be left on the ship, and often a Radio Officer could be on a ship for as long as two years. It meant that at any given time the company had a massive amount of money in its coffers, earned by and belonging to Radio Officers to make use of. Advances could be obtained at the company's offices abroad, but this was not encouraged, on the somewhat specious grounds that Radio Officers, particularly young ones, needed to be protected from themselves by expending it on high living in foreign ports.

THE GREAT RADIO OFFICER STRIKE OF 1925/6

In January 1920 Radio Officers organised a Trade Union to represent their interests under the name The Association of Wireless Telegraphists. The first Secretary was E. R. Tuck, who had joined the General Post Office in Liverpool as a telegraphist in 1887.

From 1896 onwards he was prominent in Postal Trade Unionism, and became General Secretary of the Postal Telegraphists Association in 1910.

The Association of Wireless Telegraphists was formed at the end of 1912 and in June 1918 the Association was, after lengthy negotiations, recognised by the major employers of marine wireless telegraphists, and in December 1918 he resigned from the Post Office.

In December 1919 a disagreement between the Association and the marine employers led to recognition being withdrawn by the latter, and this gave rise to the first strike of British Wireless Marine Operators. It was a short-lived affair which began on 15th June 1920, and ended on the 24th of the same month after a compromise agreement was reached. But it was a truce rather than a settlement – the Radio Officers had not achieved what they wanted, while the employers deeply resented what they had conceded. The shipowners made use of their powerful government lobby to introduce a new category of operator at sea, the 'Wireless Watcher'.

The carriage of Radio Officers in certain vessels had been made mandatory under the Wireless Telegraphy Act of 1919, much to the irritation of shipowners, and the success of the Radio Officer's brief strike prompted the government to accede to pressure to water down the safety requirement at sea by permitting the carriage of 'wireless watchers' in place of properly qualified Radio Officers. This individual was not required to hold a Postmaster General's Certificate; his function was to sit in the wireless room and listen for a possible SOS signal. This called for little more than a basic acquaintance with the Morse code, for which a 'Watcher's Certificate' was issued by the Board of Trade.

Deck Officers, who were trained in Morse signalling by lamp, were considered eminently fitted to carry out such duties as a supernumary task. But in the event, all kinds of characters appeared on ship's articles in this capacity: ordinary seamen, stewards, cadets, and even cooks.

The Association of Wireless Telegraphists immediately launched a continuing campaign to point out the inefficiency of such a system, and the danger it posed to the safety of life at sea. At the same time, the Marconi Marine Company was pressing ahead with a very sensible and practical project: the development of an 'Auto-Alarm'. This was a device which would be tuned in to the distress frequency of 500 kilocycles, and on receiving a special 'Auto-Alarm' signal (a series of suitably spaced dashes) would ring an alarm bell. Valuable though this device was, a Radio Officer was still needed to respond to the call and find out, by communicating with the distressed vessel, where it was. It was, however, an ideal device to be left switched on during a Radio Officer's off-watch period, and so it remained until Radio Officers ceased to be carried.

Throughout this period wage negotiations between the AWCT and the employers continued on their painful course. In April 1922 they broke down, only to be resumed again the following month. Finally, in the early part of 1925, the AWCT called a general strike of Radio Officers which continued in its consequences for the best part of eighteen months. Eventually, the AWCT, recognising the lobbying power of the employers, accepted a settlement very much less than they had applied for. It was a bitter experience which set the pattern for future wage negotiations until the 1939/45 War changed things at least partially.

Many Radio Officers at sea during that period had painful recollections of the strike, and those who withdrew their services often found themselves signed off ships in ports abroad and without funds or employment. Either they found some kind of job ashore or were repatriated as a 'Distressed British Seaman' by the local British Consul.

But at least one benefit had been painfully extracted from shipowners and the Board of Trade in the course of the protracted negotiations. Radio Officers became officially entitled to be described as Radio Officers rather than Wireless Operators, and were signed on Ship's Articles as such.

The name 'Association of Wireless Telegraphists' was later changed to the more appropriate name of 'Radio Officer's Union', and again later to 'The Radio and Electronic Officer's Union', after the Merchant Navy Training Board introduced the Marine Electronic Officer's Certificate.

The first journal of the Association of Wireless Telegraphists appeared under the title *The Radiograph* on 1st January 1920. In July 1921 this was changed to *The Signal*, and so it remained until the final issue in April/May/June 1985. Sadly, but aptly, the words 'Over and Out' were superimposed on the cover of this last issue. It marked the end of an era.

Then, in the early 30s, came the great British Shipping Slump, which reached a peak in 1934/5. Employers found it necessary to impose Leave Without Pay, or terminate Radio Officer's employment altogether. However, the situation was suddenly changed by the Second World War, which has been made the subject of a special chapter.

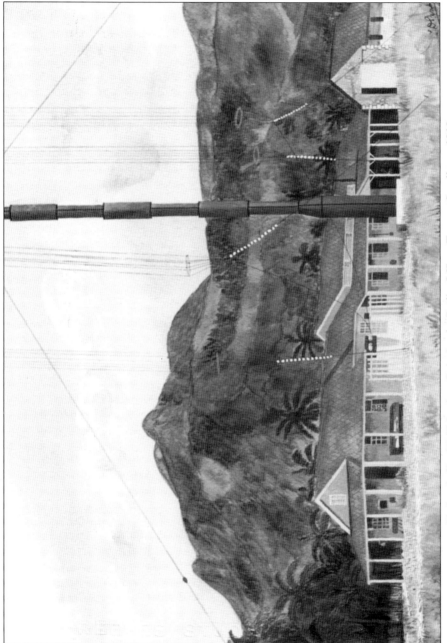

66. Seychelles W/T Station. Painting by Radio Officer Tommy Sandham, 1919.
(Photograph: Merseyside Maritime Museum)

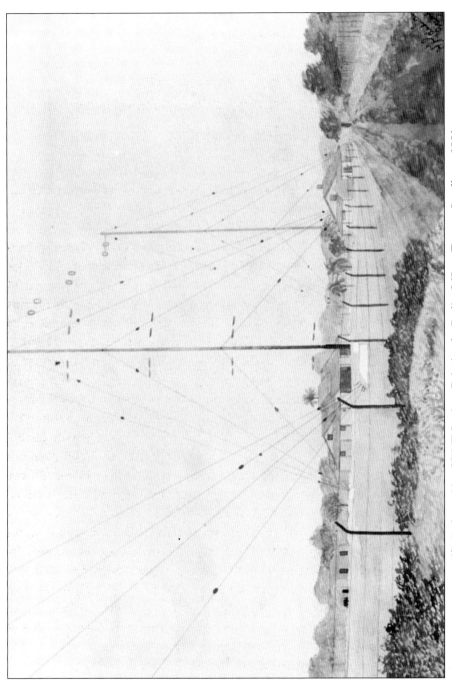

67. Bathurst Naval W/T Station. Painting by Radio Officer Tommy Sandham, 1921.
(Photograph: Merseyside Maritime Museum)

CHAPTER 6

Radio Officers and the Great Liners
of the Jazz Age

THE VERY BEGINNINGS OF WIRELESS at sea were inseparably tied up with the great liners that connected the United Kingdom to North America, India, Hong Kong and South Africa.

The good and the great and the not so good thronged the famous ships that raced across the Western Ocean carrying millionaires, film stars, crooks, politicians, lords and ladies with money to burn, and a fair proportion of well-dressed confidence men who found the restaurants and bars on board a good catchment area. Chief among these were the professional card players who haunted the North Atlantic. 'Riding the Tubs', as it was known, could be a very lucrative field of activity, particularly since a fresh crop of victims arrived with every new voyage. In the end, the shipping companies had to put up warning notices on the Purser's notice board, but they couldn't stamp it out. As Phineas Barnum, the great American showman, once re-marked: 'There's a sucker born every minute, and never give one an even break.'

When the author was working as a Technical Assistant at the Marconi Depot in Liverpool in 1950, Billy Davies, who was Marconi Radio Officer Number One, incredibly was still at sea on the *Alca*, owned by Yeowards of Liverpool and running down to Madeira. Billy had many anecdotes about his experiences as Chief Radio Officer on the first *Mauretania*. One tit-bit was that he and other Radio Officers made a lot of money on the side by taking note of stock-broking messages sent by the many financiers who sent messages about buying or selling stocks and shares. The General Post Office issued the strictest standing instructions regarding the 'Secrecy of Wireless Messages', but there was nothing to stop Billy making a wise invest-ment here and there when he got back to Liverpool.

It was said of Billy Davies that he could fill and light his pipe in the middle of writing down a message still carrying the words in his head, a feat that can only be appreciated by anyone who has tried to do it.

68. R.M.S. *Mauretania*.
(Photograph: Collection of Edward C. Heukels)

The beginnings of the Jazz Age coincided with the great days of the Western Ocean Liners, and really it continued through two decades, until the beginning of the Second World War. It began with the syncopated rhythms largely invented by coloured musicians in New Orleans which, by 1910, had emerged as 'Rag-Time'. Dancers bobbed, twisted and shuffled to Scott Joplin's 'Maple Leaf Rag'. Dixie and Jazz became enshrined in seven-piece bands like those of Duke Ellington and Benny Goodman, though most shipowners thoughtfully provided a violin quartet to cater for more elderly passengers taking their afternoon tea and pastries. On the passenger ships of the P&O and Orient Lines, the musical diet was more restrained as befitted the Empire-building ex-patriates who travelled to and from their labours supporting the 'White Man's Burden'. And all this vanished like a ghost at cockcrow in 1939.

The Radio Officers on the big ships were kept very busy indeed. Not only was there a flood of messages to and from passengers, but there was the heavy daily chore of receiving many pages of subscription press, which had to be provided to the Purser's office for inclusion in the ship's daily news-paper. In 1949, when the author was attached to the Marconi Marine Depot in Liverpool, there was working there as a contracts assistant an ex-Radio Officer called Bob Leith, who had served on the old *Lusitania* and later the *Aquitania*, who had many tales to tell of his days on the Jazz Age liners. One

"EVERYTHING'S IN ORDER, SIR."

69. *(Cartoon courtesy of Marconi plc & Norman Mansebridge)*

of his stories related to the extraordinary skill in Morse that Radio Officers serving on them developed. Several pages of press had to be received by Morse and transcribed straight on to a typewriter keyboard. Incredible as it may seem, some Radio Officers could actually read a book while they were doing this, and when the ship's newspaper came out the following morning they read it with the same degree of freshness as everybody else on board.

And then in the 30s long distance telephony added another dimension. Messages from passengers had to be handed in at the Purser's office, or on some ships a reception office attached to the Radio Office, where one of the junior Radio Officers would accept them, and count the words in order to work out the charges, the sender being required to sign his name on the back of the form. Many of the big hotels on either side of the Atlantic

'. . . and another thing: I'm always careful to leave the wireless room looking *exactly* as I found it when I joined the ship.'

70. *(Cartoon courtesy of Marconi plc & Norman Mansebridge)*

offered a wireless booking service, and paid the Wireless Operating Companies a substantial annual premium to have their advertisement spread across the whole of the back of the message form. And because the senders had to sign the back of the message form the advertisement was bound to enter their field of vision. This arrangement carried on until the mid-60s; at least ten years after it had any commercial relevance, because by then air travel was replacing the liners, except for cruising. The Savoy and the Ritz had simply been paying the Marconi Company bills because their accounting system had not picked it up, and the gravy train would have continued had not the Marconi accountants department noticed that the charges had not been increased since 1939. They promptly demanded a substantial rise in spite of the advice of the present author, whose responsibilities then included, among other things, radio traffic and accounting. Of course, that immediately drew the hotel's attention, who immediately cancelled the arrangement, and incidentally provided the author with yet another example of how accountants can ruin a company if they are not kept on a strict leash.

The great ports for the liners were Liverpool, Southampton and Tilbury in London. The crowded scenes at the Liverpool Pierhead Landing Stage and the boat trains arriving at Southampton docks from London, and long lines of Customs Searching Areas speak eloquently of the era.

Perhaps it can all be summed up best by quoting from a White Star Line Poster of 1933:

SAILING ON THE *OLYMPIC*

Pageant of fashion at the gangplank . . . fanfare and excitement . . . once again, anticipation of a delightful voyage – how well experienced travellers know the gift of gracious living White Star offers! And how wise to follow their example . . . To sail on the *Olympic* or her huge running mate, the *Majestic*, the world's largest ship. Or on England's largest cabin liners, the new *Georgic* or her sister ship, the *Britannic*. To know the White Star's spacious decks, her classic public rooms . . . to revel in every meticulous detail of White Star service, of delicious cuisine – how amazing that it costs so little!

Sadly, two years later, the *Olympic* was taken out of service for ever.

71. White Star Line R.M.S. *Olympic.*
(Photograph: National Maritime Museum)

103

72. First-class restaurant, R.M.S. *Olympic.*
(Photograph: White Star Publicity)

73. First-class lounge, R.M.S. *Olympic.*
(Photograph: White Star Publicity)

The public today is punch-drunk with descriptions of the splendour of the furnishings of the *Titanic*, but perhaps the author will be excused the indulgence of mentioning the breathtaking scale of those on the *Olympic*.

First Class passengers could choose from a variety of cabins furnished in different period styles: Jacobean, Adam and Georgian, through to the European styles of Dutch, Louis XIV and Empire. There were two palm court cafés and the main dining saloon, done out in Jacobean style, could seat 532 people at a single sitting. On the promenade deck was a mahogany panelled lounge finished in Louis Quinze mode, while the gentlemen had their own smoking room, and the ladies a reading and writing room in Georgian style.

On the *Aquitania* between the wars the 1st class menu apologised 'because the motion of the ship precluded the availability of the older red wines.' The menu listed over forty dishes.

The *Olympic* boasted the largest swimming pool afloat, and there was a gymnasium and squash court. But as Simon Mills remarks in his magnificent '*Olympic* – The Old Reliable', all this luxury was supported by the Third Class passengers, who thronged the ship as emigrants from Europe, and thus made it viable.

Then there were the famous lines that served India and the Far East: P&O, Orient, and British India Steam Navigation Lines conveying the administrators of the old British Empire and their wives to the Middle East and all points beyond. Each year they took to India what was unkindly known as the 'Fishing Fleet' – unmarried daughters of Indian Civil Servants, hoping to land an eligible bachelor. Even more unkindly the unsuccessful ones were described as 'returned empties'. Basically, India in those days was one vast system of outdoor relief for the English middle and upper classes, though it must be recorded that most served India well when they got there.

Junior Radio Officers appointed to the passenger ships which nearly always called at Bombay were very likely to be transferred to a ship permanently engaged on the Indian coastal trade. It was a cheap way by which the Marconi Company avoided the cost of sending Radio Officers out by sea (and the tiresome possibility of the victim resigning in the UK in order to avoid being separated from his family for as long as two years at a time). Just after the war, the author was attached to a British India Steam Navigation Company ship, the *Pachumba*, and was due to suffer the same fate. However, destiny intervened, for she was carried off the ship in Cardiff before it sailed suffering from smallpox, probably contracted by a visit to a fleapit local cinema. On arrival at the isolation hospital it turned out to be chickenpox – on the whole a much better alternative.

105

The tales of the adventures of Radio Officers on the Indian coast are a legion. For instance, in the late 20s, when broadcasting was first being introduced in India, J. R. Stapleton was managing the Marconi Depot in Bombay. He supplemented his income by acting as a technical consultant to the Indian founders of All India Radio. In those happy days, when ships were loaded or unloaded by derricks or coolie labour, they could easily be in port for several weeks. This meant that if say an alternator or some other piece of equipment at All India Radio broke down, Stapleton could always borrow the missing part from one of the Marconi-fitted ships in the harbour. Sometimes he kept All India Radio going for months on end by 'robbing' one ship after another. And often the borrowed part was not returned on board until the eleventh hour before sailing.

The author cannot leave India without relating the story of Stapleton's predecessor, P. B. Waterson. This gentleman began life as a Radio Officer before the First World War, but was then appointed to the Company's shore staff at Head Office in London. In due course, he was sent out to India to take charge of the Company's interests there, a task he carried out with great success. However, it was not long before temptation came his way – a frequent occurrence in India – as all who know that fascinating country will be fully aware. As well as promoting the sale of Marconi equipment, he on the side acted for one of their major English competitors. The outcome was both sad and hilarious. One day he wrote two letters – one to each company – detailing successful efforts on their respective behalfs. Unfortunately, he put the wrong letters in the wrong envelopes, and promptly received a notice of summary dismissal from the Marconi Company by return of post.

There is a postscript to the story. Waterson returned to sea as a Radio Officer on the Indian coast, where of course he was well-known to other Radio Officers on ships and coast stations. Ship stations had their own call signs, either three or later, four letters, but Waterson had his own three letter one, PBW –'Poor Bloody Waterson', as he used to explain in the club when anyone bought him a drink.

CHAPTER 7

The Loss of the 'Trevessa', 1924

THE LOSS OF THE *TREVESSA*, which foundered in the Indian Ocean on 4th June 1924, is instructive from the wireless telegraphy point of view because, paradoxically, while the distress message sent out by Radio Officer Donald J. Lamont failed to result in a rescue, it did give a major impetus to the recognition of the importance of wireless telegraphy at sea. And it is perhaps surprising to note that this was still very necessary, largely due to economy-minded shipowners.

The *Trevessa*, owned by Edward Haines & Son of St Ives in Cornwall, was a cargo vessel of 5,004 tons gross, and had been built at Flensburg in Germany for the German Hansa Line in 1909. During the 1914-18 War she was interned at Sourabaya in the Dutch East Indies. She was taken over by the Shipping Controller in August 1919 and sold to Haines. The wireless equipment had been manufactured by the Telefunken Company of Germany.

She left Fremantle, Australia, under the command of Captain Cecil Foster on 24th May 1924, bound for Antwerp, and by the 1st June had run

74. s.s. *Trevessa* at Port Pirie.
(Photograph: Cecil Miles, '1700 Miles in Open Boats', Mariner's Library, 1924)

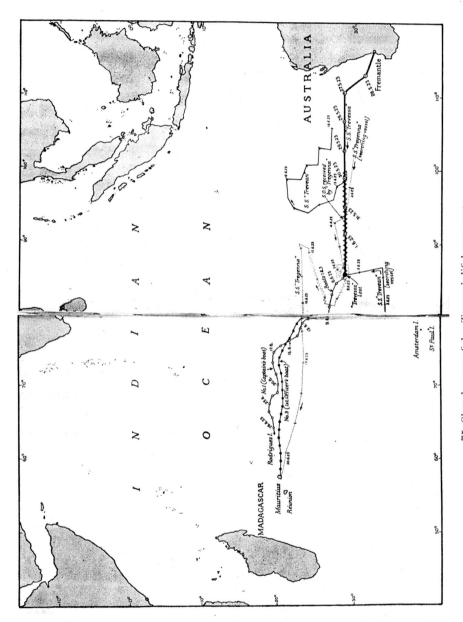

75. Sketch map of the *Trevessa*'s lifeboats route.

(Photograph: Cecil Miles, '1700 Miles in Open Boats', Mariner's Library, 1924)

76. The Officers of the *Trevessa*.
Standing, left to right: Mr Hall, 2nd Officer;
Mr Tippet, 3rd Officer; Mr Lamont, Wireless Operator.
Sitting: Captain Foster; Mr Smith, Chief Officer.
(Photograph: Cecil Miles, '1700 Miles in Open Boats', Mariner's Library, 1924)

into very heavy seas and strong winds. On 3rd June a huge sea crashed on board, tearing the two port lifeboats adrift from their lashings. By midnight the ship was labouring heavily and hove to in mountainous seas in position 28.45 South and 85.42 East. She began to make water heavily foreward, and the situation rapidly worsened.

During the *Trevessa's* long lay-up at Sourabaya the hull below the water-line had become badly encrusted with shellfish, and the discharge from these created some kind of chemical action which produced severe corrosion in the hull plates, amounting in some cases to an actual hole. Where this had occurred the holes had been drilled out and plugged with rivets.

In Captain Foster's fascinating book, *1700 Miles in Open Boats*, he expresses his belief that it was these weak spots that were responsible for the vessel foundering at 2.45 a.m. on 4th June. Their position was about 1600 miles from Fremantle and over 1,750 miles from the Mauritius Group – just about as far from land as it was possible to be.

Captain Foster had ordered Radio Officer Lamont to send out a distress message, giving the ship's position, which was answered by the s.s. *Runic*

77. Radio Officer Donald Lamont.
(Photograph: Gaynor Webber, London)

and two other ships, names unknown, because their signals were so weak. Shortly afterwards, Lamont had to join the rest of the crew in taking to the two lifeboats. One was under the command of Captain Foster and the other under the charge of the Chief Officer, James Stewart Smith. Captain Foster opted for Mauritius as offering the most favourable prospects of weather, wind and sea, even though it was further than Fremantle. After twenty-two days and nineteen hours he succeeded in reaching Rodriguez Island, and the Chief Officer's boat arrived at Mauritius after twenty-four days and twenty hours at sea. Eleven lives were lost: two in the Captain's boat and nine in the Chief Officer's, all basically from privation and sheer exhaustion.

There were other vessels within three or four hundred miles of where the *Trevessa* sank, and the part wireless telegraphy played in their efforts to reach the survivors is instructive. For an account of this, the author is indebted to the Radio Officer of the *Tregenna*, owned by the same company, and published in the *Signal* in September 1923 under the initials E.R.B.

The *Tregenna* left Port Pirie on May 19th, bound for Antwerp via Fremantle, and encountered similarly atrocious weather. As was usual between

110

the company's vessels, the Captain of the *Tregenna* had instructed his Radio Officer to get in touch with the *Trevessa*, knowing she had left Fremantle some days ahead of them. It must be remembered that in 1923 a ship fitted with a ¼ Kilowatt Spark Transmitter would only have an average range of about four to five hundred miles, given the most favourable conditions, though much greater distances could be achieved during the hours of darkness. Each night the *Trevessa* (call sign GCVJ) was heard working, but apparently did not receive the *Tregenna's* calls. Then at about 2 a.m. ship's time the *Tregenna* heard the *Trevessa* sending a distress call, which included an SOS and her position. The distance between the two ships was then about 400 miles, but although E.R.B. continued to call no reply was heard from the sinking ship.

At 2.35 a.m. the *Trevessa* broadcast that 'she was settling down by the head, and the crew were taking to the boats'. Apparently, the *Tregenna's* motion during the next twelve hours was 'almost beyond description; one continuous corkscrewing and rolling, and shipping seas with every roll'. The following night E.R.B. was able to establish communication with the s.s. *Runic*, and learned that she was 500 to 600 miles to the east of the *Trevessa's* last position.

The *Runic* then informed E.R.B. that it was in touch with another of the company's ships, the *Trevean*, bound from New York to Australia, and only about 270 miles from the *Trevessa's* last position. So heavy were the seas that the *Tregenna* could only make a headway of fifty miles in twenty-four hours, but the *Trevean*, having the weather in her favour, had by morning arrived at the spot where the *Trevessa* sank

On the morning of 6th May the *Trevean* steamed through miscellaneous floating wooden wreckage, which included an upturned jolly-boat – but not, to their relief, a lifeboat. By that time the *Tregenna* had reached the scene and the two ships worked together in convoy to cover a zig-zag searching formation, best illustrated by E.R.B. in his article (Fig 75), from which it will be seen that three other ships, *Barabool*, *Seattle* and *Port Alma*, had joined in the search.

The strong feeling of E.R.B., and indeed all who were involved in the affair, including the Authorities afterwards, was that had one of the *Trevessa's* lifeboats been fitted with a spark distress transmitter/receiver, there would have been a good chance that the two lifeboats might have been picked up within a few days, and any loss of life avoided.

The affair triggered a special Board of Trade Regulation which required certain categories of vessels to carry an emergency transmitter/receiver in one of the lifeboats. Typically, when the idea was first mooted, Mr J. Havelock Wilson, Chairman of the Seafarer's Joint Council, declared that carriage of such equipment was 'out of the question, because there was no room for it in a lifeboat'. This was in spite of the fact that such equipment had been fitted for some years on lifeboats on Cunard and White Star vessels. However, in spite of such protestations, the new regulation came into force on 1st July 1925.

By then the Marconi Company had designed a special compact lifeboat set, consisting of a quarter Kilowatt quenched gap spark transmitter and a three valve receiver working on the fixed distress frequency of 500 Kilocycles, and driven from a motor alternator. By April 1926, more than 171 such fittings had been installed.

Donald Lamont later obtained a shore appointment with Marconi Marine and was for many years attached to their Aberdeen Depot. An extract from Captain Foster's diary, made four days before his boat reached Rodriguez, describes Lamont's conduct as follows:

> 'Lamont was by this time feeling the effects of exposure very much, being only a youngster and without as much physical strength as the others. To start with he took his full share of in whatever there was to do, helping with the steering and so on. He was still keeping watch, in fact continued to do so until we reached land, but he had to be helped to sit upright, and keep in a sitting position. In spite of his weakness, however, he never grumbled or uttered a protest.'

CHAPTER 8

Radio Officers at War

WORLD WAR I

Whope acounts of the part played by Radio Officers and their many acts of heroism and self-sacrifice during World War II far exceed the space available to record them, information relating to individual Radio Officers in World War I has been more difficult to locate. The author is therefore particularly grateful to Mr Patrick Watson for kindly making available material and pictures relating to his uncle, the late Alfred Pink, who was serving on the Orient Liner *Otranto* during that vessel's encounter on 1st November 1914, with German warships at the battle of Coronel, Chile.

Radio Officer Alfred Pink was born in May 1894 in Redhill, and after leaving school became a telegraphist at Redhill Station. In July 1912 he qualified as a Radio Officer in the Merchant Navy, and his first sea-going appointment was as a junior Radio Officer on the Red Star liner *Lapland*. The *Lapland* was built in 1909 by Harland & Wolff at Belfast and carried 450 passengers 1st Class, 400 2nd Class, and 1,500 3rd Class. For most of her career she operated on the Antwerp-Dover-New York service, no doubt largely engaged in the emigrant trade. Between 1914 and 1919 she was operated by the White Star Line. Interestingly, it was on the *Lapland* that the survivors of the *Titanic* disaster were repatriated to the UK in 1912. In 1920 she reverted to the

78. Radio Officer Alfred Pink.
(Photograph: Patrick Watson,
Winston, County Durham)

113

79. The Red Star Liner *Lapland*, 1912.
(Photograph: Patrick Watson, Winston, County Durham)

North Atlantic service until 1933, when after a few Mediterranean cruises, she was sold to the Japanese and broken up.

When Alfred Pink joined her, the *Otranto* had been taken over by the Admiralty as an auxiliary cruiser, and as such was part of the British Squadron under Rear-Admiral Sir Christopher Craddock. The squadron, consisting of *Good Hope, Monmouth, Glasgow* and *Otranto*, discovered the German ships, but were hopelessly out-gunned. *Glasgow* and *Otranto* were ordered to make use of their speed to escape. The *Good Hope* and the *Monmouth* were sunk, but as a result of this action a powerful squadron under Vice-Admiral Sir Frederick Doveton Sturdee was dispatched to the South Atlantic. This led to the Battle of the Falkland Islands, in which all the German ships except the *Emden* were destroyed.

The *Otranto* made her way to Vancouver, where she underwent repairs. Her end came in October 1918 when she was wrecked after being in collision with the P&O vessel *Kashmir*.

In the early 1920s Alfred Pink was employed by the Marconi Company at their station near Caernarfon in North Wales, and possibly became its manager. This station is of historic importance because soon after Marconi's historic 'Leap Across the Atlantic' a station was set up at Clifden on the west coast of Ireland as the nearest point of contact in the UK in terms of the telegraph land-line link. This was soon after followed by the station

80. The Orient Liner *Otranto* while serving as an auxilliary cruiser in 1914 undergoing repairs in dry-dock in Vancouver.
(Photograph: Patrick Watson, Winston, County Durham)

81. The Marconi Roll of Honour, 1914-18.

(Photograph: Marconi plc)

near Caernarfon, which brings Alfred Pink into a direct connection with the early development of wireless communication between the UK and USA. In the early 1930s Alfred Pink, by then married, opened a shop in Croydon selling radio and later television sets. He died in March 1992 at Redhill, Surrey.

WORLD WAR II

From the moment that war was declared the Merchant Service found itself in the front line, and was soon and, appropriately, renamed the Merchant Navy. There was no preliminary period of 'phoney war' – only nine hours into hostilities the Donaldson liner *Athenia*, bound for the USA and carrying over 1,400 souls, was torpedoed on 5th September 1939, 200 miles off the Irish Coast. It was an ominous sign of things to come.

As much as possible of the shipping trade on the east coast was transferred to western ports, but the coastal and short sea trades had to continue in spite of E-boats, U-boats and German bombers.

In peacetime most ships, except passenger vessels, only carried one Radio Officer, who had to have either a First or Second Class Certificate, and the advent of war brought an immediate change. Transmitting, except in very special and prescribed circumstances, became immediately banned as it could attract the attention of surface raiders, but at the same time a continuous listening watch became just as important. Suddenly, there was a need for two extra Radio Officers on every single Radio Officer ship, and this could be met by the PMG 'Special' Certificate – only the Chief Radio Officer was required to hold a First or Second Class Certificate.

The losses of Radio Officers between 1939 and 1945 reflected those of the Merchant Navy as a whole. At least 1,406 Radio Officers sacrificed their lives, and of these 980 were employed by the Marconi Marine Company. Overall, approximately 180,000 men of all races and creeds sailed under the Red Ensign, and of these more than 35,000 were lost at sea. The names of 24,000 of these appear on their memorial on Tower Hill.

According to figures known to the author from her own records, which still survive at Chelmsford, the Marconi Marine Company at the end of the war employed approximately 5,500 surviving Radio Officers.

At this point the author must record her indebtedness to the late Mr Peter Barber, of Stourbridge, and his co-author, George Monk, of Crowborough, who devoted three years of patient research into collecting and collating

117

details of all those Radio Officers who lost their lives in World War II. The fruits of their labours can now be consulted in the form of bound volumes deposited in the Archives of the Liverpool Maritime Museum, which themselves offer much scope for interesting research. For instance, there were apparently four brothers who all went to sea as Radio Officers, and all but one was lost.

Mr Barber himself was serving on the *Clan MacWhirter* as third Radio Officer when on 22nd August 1941, it was torpedoed not far from Madeira, and his experiences are related in more detail later in this chapter (see page 132).

The declaration of war in 1939 came as sudden and alarming news to ships at sea and in ports all over the world. A good example of its consequences might be the experience of Radio Officer George W. Johnson, then serving on the *Ullapool*, owned by the north-east coast firm of Ropners, which at the

82. Radio Officer George Johnson and Mrs Johnson.
(Photograph: Marconi plc)

time was loading in Vancouver, British Colombia. After leaving port the ship sailed right around the west coast of North America, keeping within the three-mile limit for fear of U-boat attack, until they reached the Panama Canal. Once in the Atlantic they joined a UK-bound convoy consisting of 120 vessels, escorted by one battleship. They arrived safely, but on the next voyage the ship was sunk by a submarine in the mouth of the Humber. Fortunately, the vessel settled on a sandbank, and all the crew were rescued.

Not long after that, George was transferred to the shore technical staff of Marconi Marine, and after working in the UK for two years, spent some years attached to the company's various depots in India. Subsequently, he returned to the UK, where he successively became a Divisional Manager, Marine Director, Marconi South Africa, and Managing Director of Norsk Marconi Co A/S.

George, an old friend and ex-colleague of the author, is at the time of writing, Mayor of Colwyn Bay in North Wales, in spite of having had for many years to make use of a wheel-chair. In December 2000 he was elected 'Millennium Man of the Year'.

Almost immediately, arrangements were made to form merchant ships into convoys, which were organised and controlled by a Commodore or Vice-Commodore, who took up quarters on two ships which became the Commodore and Vice-Commodore ships respectively. Most of the Commodores were senior or retired RN Vice-Admirals or Captains, and John Slader, in his magnificent book, *The Fourth Service*, lists the names of twenty-one of these who lost their lives while sailing out of Liverpool.

Captain E. Rees RNR who was lost on the *Empire Howard* on 16th April 1942, in Convoy PQ14, might serve as a typical example. His vessel sank in less than a minute, and he was last seen in the water clinging to a piece of wooden wreckage and smoking a cigar. Miraculously, the Master of the *Empire Howard*, Captain Downie, survived.

The Arctic convoys to Murmansk and Archangel remain a nightmare for those who can remember them. The chances of rescue and survival in freezing waters was almost zero, and outside the accommodation everything froze solid. A large proportion of the ships had steam winches, and to prevent the deck lines freezing up they were kept slowly ticking over as soon as really cold weather was encountered.

There were at least sixty-two Arctic convoys, and one ship in every three was lost by enemy action. Over a hundred vessels did not survive the passage, and more than 3,000 seamen were drowned in conditions that scarcely bear thinking about.

83. A convoy during World War II.
(Photograph: H.M.S.O.)

Sydney Shacklock was serving as Chief Radio Officer of the *Auckland Star*, which was torpedoed eighty miles from coast of Eire in 1940 while on a return voyage from Australia. Fortunately, the crew were rescued and landed at Dingle the next morning. He had an even narrower escape in March 1944 while serving on the *Empire Tourist* homeward bound from Archangel. Two torpedoes simultaneously hit the vessel; fortunately, she was a light ship, and did not blow up as it would have done had she been loaded with war supplies, including ammunition. It was the only ship in the convoy to be lost, and the crew survived only because they had time to get into a lifeboat. Sydney remembers with gratitude the reception they received when boarding the escort vessel which took them on board – its Commanding

Officer was at the gangway, and shook the hand of every survivor as he came on board.

The main convoy gathering points around the UK were Loch Ewe, the Gareloch, the Clyde on the west coast, and Belfast Lough. At least that is the author's recollection, for during the war years she sailed from all of them. Also on her list is Gibraltar, Capetown, and Freetown. At all of these places the Masters of the ships in the convoy would be gathered and briefed by the Convoy Commodore on the tactics that would be employed in that particular convoy. For instance, it would probably include an order for all ships to zig-zag in an effort to foil attacks by submarines, which had developed a nasty habit of surfacing and running up between the columns of ships

Special war-time signals were introduced to be used by merchant ships which found it necessary to send a distress message. The standard peace-time distress call consisted of SOS, CQ (All Stations), name of ship, position, followed by details which often depended on how much time was available to send them. Whenever possible the Auto-Alarm Signal (see page 95) had to be sent first, to alert Radio Officers on other ships who might be off watch. In war-time, three additional signals could be used: AAA (attack by aircraft), SSS (attack by submarine), and RRR (attack by surface raider).

84. Shelled in the English Channel.
These men were under fire for over an hour from German coastal batteries between Boulogne and Calais. Theirs was the leading merchant ship of a large convoy, which came safely through. Escorting destroyers put up a protective smoke screen.
(Photograph: H.M.S.O.)

85. Rescue!
(Photograph: H.M.S.O.)

Each ship carried a code book which was bound between lead covers, and had to be thrown overboard if circumstances demanded it, and these books – within the author's experience at least – resided in the radio room, where any de-coding was done.

There is a wonderful story, possibly apocryphal, but probably true, that some naval officer left the Master Copy of one of these codes in a London taxi during the war. Consequently, all the codes had to be changed at very short notice, with the result that the German Intelligence, which had just cracked that particular code, found themselves back at square one. There is probably something to be said for the idea that if you don't know what you are doing, then nobody else does either, which in war-time might be a decided advantage.

GENERAL ORDERS, Regulation 83: '*Acceptance of messages at ports abroad from persons ashore . . is prohibited.*'

86. *(Cartoon courtesy of Marconi plc & Norman Mansebridge)*

In writing this book the author has had from time to time to decide at what point her own recollections deserve inclusion; always a difficult choice between a desirable reticence and recognising the value of a first-hand acquaintance with the subject. Usually they have been omitted, but since she sailed in many convoys during the war years, perhaps a first-hand account, fresh as it were, from the mint of memory, might not be out of place.

87. The s.s. *Lorna* (sister ship to s.s. *Lorca*, taken pre-war).

THE *LORCA* – A CONVOY TO WEST AFRICA IN 1943

The other day, while researching for another book, I received a photograph from the Hull College of Technology which showed the equipment used to teach students on the marine radio course in 1931. I looked, and then looked again; and suddenly fifty-eight years dropped away. There, screwed on a bench, was all the equipment one could expect to see on a vessel of that period. On the left was a 1½ Kilowatt Valve Transmitter; then came a Direction-Finder, Two Valve Receiver, Auto-Alarm, and a ¼ Kilowatt Quench Gap Spark Transmitter. Under the bench and fixed to walls was a supporting assembly of motor-alternators, charging boards, and accumulators. Fascinated, I realised that I was looking, with the exception of the valve transmitter, at all the equipment fitted on the steam tramp *Lorca*, which I joined early in 1943 in Middlesbrough. As I write this it seems as yesterday, so clearly do I remember signing articles on a damp, freezing, foggy morning;

the sort of weather with which the north-east coast regularly fortifies her children.

In those days ship's crews were signed on the Articles by the Master, under the supervisory eye of the Shipping Master. Like most shipping offices in the big ports the counter had a heavy brass grill screwed on its top; this was because the shipping clerks tended to be so superior and offensive to crews that it was necessary for their protection.

I signed as Chief Radio Officer, even though I was still only eighteen years old; so many Radio Officers had been lost since the war started that the authorities were scraping the bottom of the barrel. In war-time one grows up quickly, a blessing I have been thankful for all my life. Next morning we were steaming up the North Sea, bound for North Shields and Smith's Dry Dock, no junior Radio Officers being deemed necessary for the short trip.

The *Lorca*, built in 1925, was what was termed a 'three-island ship' with a raised forecastle, well-deck hatches, midships accommodation for the officers and stewards, more well-deck hatches, and a raised after section. Owned by Cory Brothers, the north-east coast Coal and Bunkering Agents, she had, like the rest of the Merchant Service, been taken over by the Ministry of War Transport.

How fortunate I was to have experienced the *Lorca*! She was a mint specimen of her period, and the carpenter who sailed on her had worked on the ship when she was built, and been on her ever since. He had all sorts of anecdotes about the ship; one that I particularly remember was that the electric bulb on the top of the foremast had never needed changing since the ship was built.

The woodwork and brasswork in the accommodation was a sight to behold; heavy mahogany and polished brass everywhere. The Saloon, where the officers had their meals, and which also served as a social centre, was a mass of cut glass and gleaming mahogany.

Overhead hung two ornate brass lamps suspended in gimbals. All the cabins has brass lamps – 'Paraffin Dynamos', as we used to call them. The ship had electric light of course, but before the war this was generally shut down in port by the owner's orders in order to save the coal which would be used by the donkey engine generator.

The Saloon and Radio Room were heated by coal stoves called 'bogies'; the one in the Radio Room being much in demand for all the officers to hang their clothes around to dry after washing them in a bucket in the usual way.

125

88. The convoy conference.
(Photograph: H.M.S.O.)

The crew all lived in the forecastle which was divided in two; sailors on one side, and firemen on the other, and each had their own toilet facing aft. They tended to leave the doors open unless the weather was very bad because there was no electric light. My own cabin was a delight to me. It was situated on the port side with a big coaming over which one stepped straight out on the deck. Right through the centre went a brass casing round the chimney from the saloon fire. I was always snug but got burned when heavy weather threw me against it.

I cannot remember what cargo we loaded after leaving North Shields; probably we went out light ship, for the purpose of the ship was to load manganese ore at Pepel, which lay up the river above Freetown.

From the Tyne we sailed north about to the convoy gathering point, which in that case was Loch Ewe. There I went ashore with the Master, he to the Master's conference, I to the Radio Officers. There, along with the others, I was briefed on what codes and special signals would be employed by the convoy Commodore in the event of U-boat attacks, and it was explained that the convoy would take a wide sweep out into the South Atlantic before heading in for the convoy gathering point at Freetown.

Freetown at that time was an important convoy gathering port for the eastern South Atlantic, and the harbour was full of ships at anchor in the stream, when we arrived. It was always interesting to watch other ships coming in, no doubt congratulating themselves as we had for avoiding the

89. A convoy gathering at Freetown, Sierra Leone.
(Photograph: H.M.S.O.)

90. Caught alone in the South Atlantic.
(Photograph: H.M.S.O.)

91. A last hold on life.
(Photograph: H.M.S.O.)

German U-boats which were sustained at sea by the Vichy Government-controlled French port of Dakar.

How we cursed the name of Petain! Ships loaded as we would be, if torpedoed in the foreward hatches, sink like stones. They just carried on steaming straight under the surface, and probably only the people on the bridge or deck might get off, if they were lucky. And then they had to escape the sharks which followed the ships, attracted by the galley refuse.

One of the sights of Freetown in 1943 was the old Union Castle Liner, the *Edinburgh Castle*, then more or less an immobile wreck awaiting eventual breaking up. But during the war it served as a very convenient base for authorities, and it was popularly believed that she was firmly aground on empty beer cans and whisky bottles!

The manganese wharf at Pepel was a day's steaming up the Sierra Leone River, around twisting bends along a swirling, muddy waterway, lined with dense tropical forest which wound its way into the heart of the Dark Continent. What you get in that part of the world is a combination of insufferable heat, drenching rain; the ship becomes a sort of furnace, and the perspiration which pours off you seems to cling to the skin and smell.

There is something about Africa which I cannot define rationally. I think it springs from my youthful recollection of that river; I have a sense of innate hostility to fair society which sadly seems to neutralise the efforts of that minority of European educated idealists struggling to bring order and an end to black Africa.

I still have vivid memories of the old *Lorca*. It was on her in my late teens that I learned to play pontoon, solo-whist, and stud poker, sitting at the long green-baize covered saloon table. The Chief Engineer was a great one for cards. He had a huge belly that he could scarcely wedge in front of the table, which he used to pat, and shout 'Forty years of wasted life!' But his life wasn't wasted; those old time Chief Engineers knew everything about their job from turning up something on the lathe to weighing sacks of coal.

Across the years I salute my old friends, and gratefully acknowledge how much I owe to them. I see them now across a distance of more than fifty years, very clearly, but as if they are a long way off, like looking through the wrong end of a telescope. And what I remember is not the U-boats and the sinkings, but crowding round in each other's cabins with a case of twenty-four cans of Barclays beer on the floor, the air thick with cigarette smoke and telling the hoary old jokes that everybody knew by heart but never tired of telling, and above all, the laughter.

129

RADIO OFFICER MAURICE GLOVER –
AN ENCOUNTER WITH TWO SUBMARINES, 1942

Radio Officer Maurice Glover joined the s.s. *Elmdale* on 31st December 1941, in Barrow-in-Furness. She was a typical general cargo vessel, built for her owners, the Morriston Steamship Company Ltd., of Newcastle-on-Tyne.

92. Radio Officer Maurice Glover and his wife Joyce
on honeymoon in Torquay, September 1945.
(Photograph: Maurice Glover)

They sailed in convoy to Durban, South Africa, with a cargo destined for Singapore in the form of shells, bombs, ammunition, land-mines, and army trucks. They left Durban bound for Colombo, but en route received orders to proceed to Bombay. There they discharged part of the their cargo, and the remainder in Karachi. They were then ordered to Colombo via Bombay, and when about three hundred miles from Ceylon received dozens of distress messages sent by ships in the Bay of Bengal which were being attacked by Japanese battleships, cruisers, aircraft-carriers and aircraft.

At about 1 a.m. on 7th April, on a clear half-moonlight night, they began to be shelled by a Japanese submarine. The first shell struck the *Elmdale* amidships, and Maurice Glover managed to send off a distress message to Colombo. The starboard lifeboat was destroyed, and the cabins amidships reduced to matchwood; and while another message was in the process of being sent, the radio room was damaged by another shell, which put the equipment out of action and brought down the aerial. Apparently the submarine had fired a torpedo, which had missed the ship, and by then the Master of the *Elmdale* had commenced zig-zagging, so that they were able to make their way to Colombo.

From there they joined a convoy to Durban and then another to New York, from where they went on to Baltimore to load a general cargo which included two railway locomotives welded to the deck with chains, and a great deal of railway material. This was destined for Egypt in order to implement plans to build a railway line from Egypt to Benghazi (which never materialised!).

They left Trinidad as part of a convoy of eight ships when on Sunday, 1st November, they were hit by a torpedo amidships on the starboard side

Maurice Glover managed to send out a distress call – RRR (raider) SSS (submarine) *Elmdale* 00.17N, 34.55W torpedoed 2108 GMT. It was not long before the ship began to settle, and the boat-deck was awash. There was a life-raft on the boat-deck, secured by a rope, and he had just managed to cut through this with a knife, when he was sucked under the water. Struggling to the surface, he managed to get on to the raft, and began to paddle it towards a red light he could see some distance away. To his delight it turned out to be the standard light attached to a life-jacket by his Second Radio Officer, Alec MacNaught.

After some time, they were picked up by the *Elmdale*'s motor-lifeboat which had been cruising around picking up other survivors. While this was going on, the U-boat came alongside, and its captain, in very good English, hailed them, saying: 'There is no danger.'

There were thirty-six survivors in the lifeboat, and after six days they were sighted by a Catalina flying-boat, which dropped supplies of food and sent for help. This arrived in the form a Brazilian cargo vessel which took them to Fortelaza. From there they were sent to New York, and eventually arrived back in the UK aboard a tanker in March 1943.

There is a fascinating sequel to Maurice Glover's story; for after the war he got in touch with the captain of U-boat 174, Captain Ulrich Thilo, and they began a friendship which lasted until the latter's death in 1980. When that occurred Captain Thilo's widow sent Maurice a photograph of her late husband, which remains a treasured possession. Mr Glover and his wife are still in good health, and living in retirement in Warrington.

RADIO OFFICER PETER BARBER, AND THE LOSS
OF THE *CLAN MacWHIRTER*

In January 1941 Peter Barber joined the *Clan MacWhirter*, his first ship, as third Radio Officer. After loading military equipment, ammunition and high octane in drums, the vessel sailed for Singapore, virtually a floating ammunition dump. On arrival at Capetown they were re-directed to Durban for bunkers and because in the meantime Singapore had fallen the orders were changed to Karachi. After discharging there, they loaded in Bombay,

93. Radio Officer Peter Barber of the *Clan MacWhirter*, 1942.
(Photograph: Peter Barber)

94. The *Clan MacWhirter.*
(Photograph: Peter Barber and John Clarkson, Preston)

Lourenço Marques and Capetown with a mixed cargo for the UK, and eventually arrived at Freetown in August 1942 where they joined a home-ward bound convoy.

The *Clan MacWhirter* was the leading vessel in the convoy, which consisted of eleven ships, but on 19th August she developed engine trouble, and fell behind the convoy. On 20th August the Chief Radio Officer received a coded message from GBR, the UK Long Distance Radio Station, instructing them to sail on a completely new route, which would be subject to a 24-hour change; this meant that the ship was then officially a 'straggler'. By 26th August, when they were about 145 miles from Madeira, the ship was hit by two torpedoes, and sank within six minutes by the stern.

Peter Barber went into the radio room where the Chief Radio Officer, John Lewis, was transmitting at the Morse key, and told him to 'B ..... off.' Barber had just got into the captain's boat, now in the water, when the ship went down with a terrific roar. The boat, which had not been able to cast off, was upturned, and Barber felt himself dragged down by suction. After what seemed an age he was suddenly being shot to the surface, where he found the Chief Officer sitting aboard an upturned lifeboat and directing survivors to a life-raft, which he managed to board. The life-raft was packed with Lascars, and Barber decided to swim back towards the Chief Officer's

133

boat. But before reaching it he was hauled aboard a second lifeboat under the command of the Second Officer. This picked up the Chief Officer, who naturally assumed command, and while they were in the process of picking up other survivors, the U-boat, which he later discovered was U-156, came alongside.

The captain of the U-boat, Lt. Commander Werner Hartenstein, then gave them a course for Madeira, wished them good night, and departed. Three lifeboats altogether had survived, and a roll call determined that ten members of the crew had been lost, including the captain, Roderick S. Masters, and the Chief Radio Officer; all presumed drowned.

By the afternoon of the 27th the wind had risen to full gale force, which eventually moderated by the 29th. On the 1st September the third engineer remarked that he thought he could see land on the starboard side, and Peter Barber and the Second Radio Officer decided to send out an SOS message on the lifeboat transmitter.

Almost immediately they received an answer from CUB, Funchal Radio, and not long after that they were picked up by the Portuguese patrol vessel, *Pedro Nunes*. From there they were shipped to Lisbon, where a Belgian coaster, the *Rene Paul*, took them to Gibraltar. From Gibraltar, Barber, the Second Radio Officer and an apprentice were put aboard the *Miriam* to work their way home. Also on the *Miriam* were some survivors from the tanker *Ohio*, which had been one of only three ships to survive the 'Pedastel' convoy to Malta.

Werner Hartenstein was born in Saxony in 1910 and died when his submarine *March* was lost in March 1943, aged thirty-three. Incidentally, it was he, when commanding the U-156 torpedoed the *Laconia* on 11th September 1942, who had got into trouble with Admiral Doenitz for surfacing to see what he could do to help the survivors of the *Laconia*.

This incident led directly to Doentiz's infamous order to all U-boats – the *Laconia* Order of 1942, which led to his sentence at Nuremburg for ten years because of war crimes.

In July 2001 Miss Louise Weymouth, the Archivist of Marconi plc, received a letter from Mrs A. E. Bristow of Seaton, in Devon, which enclosed three letters and a photograph. They had turned up in a box from a boot sale, and Mrs Bristow deserves eternal credit for preserving them; sadly, they must have been of no interest to the family who discarded them.

They relate to Radio Officer John Clarkson of Manchester who joined the Marconi Marine Company on 14th August 1940, and was appointed to

95. Radio Officer John Clarkson – torpedoed three times.
(Photograph: Marconi plc and Mrs A. E. Bristow)

the *Dalcairn*. On 21st September the ship was sunk by enemy action, and as his Record Card (which still exists) shows, he was landed at Greenock four days later. On 15th November he joined the *Nalgora*, which was torpedoed on 2nd January 1941, Clarkson being landed in Freetown a week later. The Record Card gives no details of what happened during that week, and indicates that Clarkson returned to the UK as a passenger on the s.s. *Orion*, reporting at Glasgow on 3rd February.

One month later he was back at sea, and served on three other ships before joining the s.s. *Ocean Seaman* on 28th January 1943, and was again torpedoed. This time the vessel was able to be towed into Algiers though it subsequently became a total loss by German bombing. He was repatriated in the *Fort Confidence*, arriving in Leith on 26th April 1943. He spent the rest of the war at sea, and resigned, no doubt rather thankfully, on 19th December 1945.

The three letters from the Assistant General Manager of the Marconi Marine Company, S. Stansbridge (who, as it happens, was the writer's predecessor), offer their congratulations on his survival, and the last one ends as follows:

'Notwithstanding that the hopes we expressed after your previous mishaps have not been realised, we tender to you our earnest good wishes for a safe homecoming from all your future voyages.'

135

It is sad that his photograph (Plate 95) and letters do not remain the treasured possessions of a surviving family; perhaps fate decided a more lasting record in the form of this book.

The list of Radio Officers who distinguished themselves or gave their lives during World War II is so long that it would exhaust the reader, and perhaps by sheer repetition, reduce the impact. The few incidents which follow are merely representative of many, rather than being more heroic than others who have not been mentioned.

The first impact of hostilities was felt on the short-sea routes around the UK, and especially in the North Sea. One of the first to suffer was the s.s. *Keynes*, a collier owned by Stephenson Clark and Associated Companies. Her defence equipment consisted of one Lewis gun, and she was attacked twice in one day by a Heinkel III which dropped six bombs, all of which missed. Three Spitfires then came to their rescue, but the Heinkel dropped three more bombs, one of which blew much of the port side away and set the ship on fire, and at the same time put the steering gear out of action. The Radio Officer, C. A. Coleman, though severely wounded, continued to send out distress signals, until he joined the rest of the crew in abandoning ship. They were later picked up by a naval vessel, and Mr Coleman in due course received an MBE and was awarded the Lloyd's War Medal for his courageous action.

One of the first passenger liners to be torpedoed was the Donaldson Liner *Athenia*, sunk on the 5th September 1939. The Radio Officers in one of HM transports, which was in the vicinity, paid tribute to the 'cool and decisive manner' in which the Radio Officer of the *Athenia* had transmitted the distress message. Before abandoning the ship, he had the foresight to screw down the key of the emergency transmitter, which enabled other vessels in the vicinity to take continuous direction-finder bearings, which lasted for an hour until the vessel sank.

Surface raiders, until they were finally disposed of by the Royal Navy, were a terrible threat, particularly to lone ships travelling independently. One of these was the *Port Brisbane*, hit by a surface raider's salvoes which penetrated the engine room and also put the steering gear out of action. The raider sent a boarding party, who placed bombs in the engine room and stokehold, and the surviving crew were taken prisoner. The Chief Radio Officer, J. H. Magee, though badly wounded and suffering from burns, continued to send out distress signals 'in the face of persistent fire from the enemy'. He died whilst a prisoner-of-war, and was posthumously awarded a Lloyd's War Medal.

The *King John*, on a passage from the UK to Vancouver, was hit by a salvo of shells from a surface raider, which put the steering out of action and reduced the vessel to a mass of wreckage foreward and amidships, and set the stern on fire. The Chief Radio Officer, Dudley Haslam Golden, continued at his post until the aerial was brought down by enemy fire and was subsequently awarded the MBE, while the Second Radio Officer received the King's Commendation.

The *Baron Cochrane* was torpedoed and had to be abandoned. The survivors got away in one lifeboat and two rafts, the Chief Radio Officer, Charles Scott Marshall, remaining on board until the last moment before the ship sank.

Of course the instances of Radio Officer's heroism did not end with World War II, and this book would be incomplete if it did not mention the heroic conduct of Radio Officer Broadbent, who lost his life when the Larne-Stranraer ferry *Princess Victoria* foundered on 31st January 1953.

Operated by British Railways, the *Princess Victoria*, 2,694 tons and built by W. Denny & Bros at Kilmarnock in 1947, was leaving Loch Ryan when the full force of a gale caused a tremendous sea to strike the stern door and flood the car deck. Some of the boats were smashed, although two were not, and it was not long before the vessel capsized and foundered. The vessel was about four miles east of the Copeland Islands off the coast of County Down, and of the 172 crew and passengers, only forty-four survived, to be landed by the Donaghadee life-boat at Donaghadee.

The Captain and all the officers, including Radio Officer Broadbent, were lost and Mr H. Jardine, who was at the time the Radio Officer at Port Patrick Radio who controlled the distress working, and later Chief W/T Surveyor in Liverpool, paid tribute to the coolness and courage or R/O Broadbent, who was posthumously awarded the George Cross.

And so the list goes on, almost, it seems to the author, endlessly. A full list of awards to Radio Officers for Gallantry at Sea appeared in the *London Gazette* and *Lloyd's List* and is reproduced in Appendix 10.

*

There was of course, a third war; though not a world war – the 1982 conflict in the Falkland Islands – which was the scene of Britain's last colonial war. Together with the Royal Navy, vessels of the Royal Fleet Auxiliary and Merchant Navy played an important part, and naturally radio-communications lay at the centre of successful operations. The author must confess to having more than a passing interest at the time, being attached to the Sealink Harwich/Hook of Holland Ferry *St Edmund*, then serving as a troopship, as Chief Radio Officer for eight months, 1982/3.

96. The yacht *Elettra* at Penzance during experiments for Marconi's 'beam system'.
(Photograph: Marconi plc)

CHAPTER 9

The First Radio Officer to own a Yacht
– Marconi and the 'Elettra'

MARCONI LOVED THE SEA, and in 1920 he purchased the *Elettra*, a luxury yacht, built in May 1904 for the Archduchess Marie Theresa of Austria by Ramage & Ferguson of Leith. Designed by Cox & King of London, and originally named the *Rovenska*, she was 730 tons gross and 220 feet long, with a beam of 27½ feet and a draught of 16½ feet. She was purchased by a Mr Pratt in 1914, and promptly requisitioned by the British Admiralty, who converted her into a mine-sweeper.

Her name, *Elettra*, had been the subject of many family conferences. Marconi had first favoured *Scintilla*, the Italian for spark, but in the end changed his mind because he thought the English would pronounce it 'Sintilla'. *Elettra*, he thought, was indestructible in any language.

His new acquisition had several major advantages, the chief being the opportunities the vessel would present for use as a floating laboratory and for experiments in long distance communication. He was becoming increasingly interested in developing short waves for this purpose, and the yacht was ideal. It would fulfil his ever-pressing need for privacy and quiet to carry out his experiments in peace, and away from distractions and prying eyes. And in his latter years, when female companionship had rather taken over from the experiments, the privacy aspect was even more of an advantage.

But all that was in the future; the wireless room on the *Elettra* became the scene of major developments in short wave radio and beam aerials, and the evolution of radio-telephony and broadcasting.

On one of his earliest voyages in the *Elettra* his guests were dancing in the Bay of Biscay to a direct broadcast by the Savoy Orpheans in London, and in mid-Atlantic they heard the incomparable voice of Melba singing from Covent Garden, which Marconi re-broadcast to other stations in Europe.

97. Marconi in the Radio Room of the *Elettra*, c.1924.
(Photograph: Marconi plc)

In her fascinating book, *My Father, Marconi*, his daughter Degna describes the accommodation and life on board:

> 'From the wireless cabin rose the persistent odour of chemicals, while from the chart room came a particular pungent scent. From the galley floated the comfortable odour of good food. Inevitably, the small main saloon smelled stuffy.'

Degna's favourite room was the dining saloon, which was the biggest room of all, with generous windows that looked out across a narrow deck to the sea and sky.

The *Elettra* was based at Southampton as her home port, and cruised extensively, her first transatlantic crossing being made in 1922. The visitor's book on board was filled with the names of the hundreds of distinguished people who visited the ship, including Kings and Queens, and Marconi's study on board contained many of their signed portraits

Today, it is taken for granted that passengers or crew on board ship can have telephone conversations with the shore by simply dialling a number, but in the mid-20s it seemed extraordinary that Marconi could speak from his yacht to telephone subscribers in Australia, Canada, North and South America, Argentina and Brazil.

On 26th March 1930, he opened a radio and electronic exhibition in Sydney, Australia, directly from the *Elettra*, which was at anchor off Genoa, more than 9,000 miles away. When he pressed a key in the radio room, 3,000 electric lamps lit up at the Sydney gathering, his signals being picked up by the receiving station at Dorchester in England, from where it was relayed by beam transmission and land-line to Sydney.

On Marconi's death in July 1937 the *Elettra* was purchased by the Italian government, his executors refusing an offer of £200,000 from a would-be American buyer. The wireless equipment on board was the joint property of the Italian Marconi Company and the Marconi Company of London, and both companies joined in presenting it to the Italian government in honour of their illustrious founder.

98. The Radio Room on the *Elettra*, 1928.
(Photograph: Marconi plc)

141

99. *Elettra II*, the demonstration yacht of the Marconi International
Marine Communication Co. Ltd., c.1965.
(Photograph: Marconi plc)

When the Second World War broke out the *Elettra* had been lying neglected for three years and in 1940 she was laid up in Trieste. She was then commandeered by the Germans and sunk while on a patrol off the Dalmatian coast of Yugoslavia. After the war, Marshal Tito ordered her to be salvaged and presented to the Italian government as a token of goodwill.

The Italian government neglected her badly and, by 1971, she was a mass of rust and neglect, and leaking like a sieve. Finally, in 1978 a decision was made which ended the historic old vessel's career in a most undignified manner. She was cut up into three sections; the bow went to the Marconi Foundation in Turin, the midships section to to the Telecommunications Ministry in Rome, and the stern to the satellite earth station at Fucino. Sic Transit Gloria Mundi!

In 1962 the Marconi International Marine Communication Company commissioned the *Elettra II*, specially built for use as a demonstration vessel by the Fairmile Company at Berwick-on-Tweed. In 1966 she was disposed of, being replaced by the ignominious alternative of a lorry and trailer.

CHAPTER 10

Women Radio Officers

THE FIRST WOMAN TO BE APPOINTED to a British ship was a Canadian named Dallas Bradshaw, who was employed by the Marconi International Marine Communication Company Ltd in August 1970. As it happens, it was the author who appointed her, after approaching the Glasgow shipping company, Denholm Ship Management Ltd, who gave the idea their enthusiastic support. Fortuitously, Denholm's were at this time also blazing a trail with the first women deck apprentices. Thereafter, the number of women radio and deck officers steadily increased, and many of the latter have since achieved command, a notable example being Barbara Campbell, who after serving her apprenticeship with the P&O obtained a Master's Certificate. In due course she followed this

100. Radio Officer Dallas Bradshaw.
(Photograph: Marconi plc and Denholm Ship Management Ltd.)

up with a Square Rig endorsement, and after sailing as Mate of a full rigged ship for three years is currently commanding the sail training ship *Stavros Niarchos*.

Dallas Bradshaw was brought up in the small town of Penticton, in British Columbia, not far from the US border. The idea of going to sea never occurred to her until she was working in Port Alberni on Vancouver Island between 1960 and 1964.

She became a journalist, but one day was offered the chance to join a Norwegian ship as a stewardess. She gave up her flat, put her furniture in store, and went down to join the ship. She arrived only to find that the vacancy had been filled by someone else, so that she found herself with no

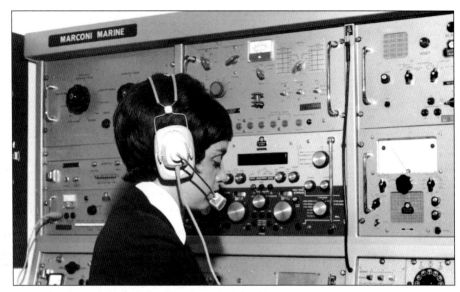

101. Dallas Bradshaw, the first woman Radio Officer to be appointed to a British vessel.
(Photograph: Marconi plc and Denholm Ship Management Ltd.)

102. Radio Officer Bradshaw meets Captain A. J. Macdonald,
Master of the 15,000-ton *Duncraig*, at the commencement
of her first working voyage.
(Photograph: Marconi plc and Denholm Ship Management Ltd.)

job, no home and not a lot of money. As it happened, a boy friend was travelling to the UK and invited her to accompany him.

They managed to get a passage on a Head Line general cargo ship called the *Roonagh Head*, which arrived in Liverpool in the middle of the night in March 1965.

Not long after they arrived, Dallas happened to see an advertisement in the *Daily Telegraph* for Radio Officers in the Merchant Navy, and this gave her the idea of training as a Radio Officer.

She became a student at The Wireless College, Colwyn Bay, in North Wales, where she literally worked her way through college, doing any part-time work she could find. At one point she found that she could not pay the college fees and keep herself at the same time, which meant that she had to be out of the college for two and a half terms. Fortunately, during this period the owner of the school, Bill Whale, the son of Gordon S. Whale, who founded it, helped by supplying her with test papers which he marked and returned. Bill later told Dallas that of all the people who'd left the college with the intention of returning, she was the only one who ever did. Fortunately, the Morse code came very easily to her, and what might have been a major hurdle did not create much of a problem.

After obtaining her PMG Certificate she applied to various employers, including the Marconi Marine Company, without success. Prospects were beginning to look gloomy, because her Certificate had to be utilised within two years of its issue, but fortunately the Marconi Company, who by then had been able to arrange with certain shipowners to accept women Radio Officers, offered her an appointment, which she accepted.

Her first ship was the *Duncraig*, owned by Denholm's Ship Management Ltd, which she joined in Middlesbrough for a voyage to Narvik. There was a great deal of advance publicity, which included a press conference and a trip to the *Dunkyle* (the sister ship to the *Duncraig*) for various photo opportunities.

She was a guest of the 'Merchant Navy' programme, from which Captain Macdonald first heard that she was going to join his ship. On the day of joining the *Duncraig* there was a press posse of about seven or eight reporters, plus the BBC and ITV. In fact, Dallas had to go up the gangway twice, once for each camera crew.

By 1982 the Marconi Marine Company was having to drastically reduce its sea staff because of the decline in the numbers of British-manned ships, and Dallas, along with many others, was made redundant.

Again fate intervened, for she happened to see an advertisement in the

Daily Express for a Radio Officer for the British Antarctic Survey vessel, *John Biscoe*. When Dallas was interviewed by them her first question was, 'Do the British Antarctic Survey offer equal opportunities to women?' At the time, this was somewhat of a social hot potato, and it had occurred to Dallas that it might not be a bad idea to raise the point. Whatever the reason, she got the job, being one out of three applicants, and became the first woman to be appointed to the British Antarctic Survey.

Her reception from the Captain and other officers was at first rather lukewarm, but things improved, and Dallas was sorry when her eighteen months period of service came to an end, perhaps not least because the prospects of getting another job as a Radio Officer were not very good. For a time, Dallas, a survivor and never afraid of hard work, cut up sandwiches in a café until she joined the North Wales Police in 1990, where at the time of writing she is still working.

Another woman Radio Officer to be appointed by Marconi Marine was Alice Mollison (now Mrs Cathro), a native of Nantwich, and who was also appointed to a Denholm vessel, the *Avon Bridge*. After obtaining eleven 'O' levels at school, Alice attended Wray Castle, the wireless

103. Radio Officer Alice Mollison, 1973.
(Photograph: Marconi plc and Denholm Ship Management Ltd.

college in the Lake District, where she obtained her PMG Certificate to become a Radio Officer. Alice was not, however, following any family seafaring tradition, her father being the director of a veterinary firm. At the age of nineteen, while on leave from her ship, Alice entered the local beauty competition, and was crowned 'Miss Nantwich', a somewhat unusual accomplishment for a Merchant Navy Officer!

104. Radio Officer Mollison on leave from the *Avon Bridge* as 'Miss Nantwich', 1973.
(Photograph: Marconi plc and Denholm Ship Management Ltd.

105. Radio Officer Joan
Wareing on board the
Edenbridge.
*(Photograph: Marconi plc
and Denholm Ship
Management Ltd.*

106. Miss Jocelyn Parker,
Radio Officer and
subsequently Marine
Electronics Technician,
Marconi Marine Company.
East Ham, London,
December 1977.
(Photograph: Marconi plc)

107. Marylynn Stockwell,
the first Irish woman
Radio Officer appointed
by Marconi plc.
(Photograph: Marconi plc)

Alice is currently living in Texas with her husband and grown-up family. Not surprisingly, he is a retired ship's Master, now with extensive business interests ashore, whom she first met when she was travelling out to join her first ship, he being at the time Second Mate.

Another woman Radio Officer was Joan Wareing, who was trained at the British School of Telegraphy, London, and in June 1973 flew out to join the *Edenbridge* at the oil port of Porvoo in Finland. From there she went to the Persian Gulf and then down to Chile. The universal form of address for a Radio Officer on board is 'Sparks' and Joan recalls that while serving the statutory preliminary period of service as a junior Radio Officer she was, perhaps inevitably, referred to as the 'Sparklet'.

Radio Officers employed by Marconi Marine were often offered a shore appointment within the company, which could lead to substantial progress in the company hierarchy. Jocelyn Parker, who trained at the Northern Counties Radio School in Preston, joined the Marconi Marine Company in September 1973 and later became one of the company's highly-trained Radio Officers. After serving at sea in the Ellerman Line, Denholm Ship Management, Ben Line, Texaco and Esso she was appointed to the shore staff at East Ham as a marine electronics technician in December 1977.

The first Irishwoman to be appointed by Marconi Marine was Marylynn Stockwell, from Tuam, in County Galway. She joined Irish Shipping Ltd.'s ship *Irish Maple* for her preliminary sea training in October 1973.

Carole Langley spent eight and a half years as a Radio Officer employed by Marconi Marine until she was made redundant in 1985, and the story of how she came to obtain a PMG Certificate is fascinating and, to say the least, unusual.

In 1975 Carole Langley was a lecturer in Hull Technical College, her subject being General Studies for Apprentices (the equivalent of the current Core Skills and Psychology for Nurses). In the course of her work, she came across five individuals who seemed to enjoy their work, and they were Radio Officers in the Merchant Navy. It led her to switch jobs and go to sea as a Radio Officer.

The training course at that time was two and a half years. Carole approached the head of the marine radio training course at the college, who agreed, somewhat dubiously, to accept her for an accelerated training course of one year, which of course included reaching the required Morse code standard. Incredibly, she not only successfully passed the PMG examination, but by studying for an extra term obtained the Radar Maintenance Certificate and the City & Guilds T4 in Radio Theory. To complete all this in four terms must probably stand as a record, and possibly Carole was the only Radio Officer to go to the sea with a degree in Psychology!

In 1985 she took voluntary redundancy from Marconi Marine, and was accepted by Lancaster University to study for an M.A. in Organisational Analysis. Since then she has obtained a Ph.D. and is now a researcher into non-clinical health issues.

CHAPTER 11

Radio Officers on Deep-Sea Trawlers
– Black Ice and the Greenland Seas

A Note on Terminology: As has been stated previously, the early practitioners of the art of wireless telegraphy at sea were invariably referred to as 'Wireless Operators', or more familiarly as 'Sparks', but by the 1940s the term 'Radio Officer' was used, except by a minority of ship's Masters who felt it added to their own importance to deprive them of the title of Officer. On trawlers, this application of terminology did not apply; the radioman was a 'Wireless Operator' just as there was the 'Skipper', 'Mates', 'Engineers' and 'Deckie-Learners'. But in this chapter, for convenience in the overall context of this book, the term 'Radio Officer' is used.

THE FIRST FITTINGS ON TRAWLERS

THE USE OF WIRELESS TELEGRAPHY on deep-sea trawlers, which was soon followed by Direction-Finders, Echo-Sounders, Radio Telephony and, in due course, Radar, is of particular interest, because outside of the fishing industry it is not generally appreciated just how skilful the Radio Officers on trawlers were, and how much they contributed towards the success of the voyage. From the beginning, deep-sea trawlers carried not just as much, but usually a great deal more than the average deep-sea ship, including liners, where of course the wireless traffic would be heavy. On deep-sea cargo ships or tankers there would be relatively few messages: just those relating to departures and arrivals, messages between the Master and his owners, and to agents regarding the cargo. For the rest the Radio Officer occupied himself by maintaining the Statutory Safety Watch, and such routine matters as weather reports, navigational warnings and a few private messages to and from the crew.

Things on trawlers were quite different; every piece of equipment, especially the Direction Finder, Echo-Sounder and Radar was in constant use. Just as important was the ability of the Radio Officer to repair, and quickly,

108. The steam trawler *Bardolph.*
(Photograph: Maritime Museum, Hull)

anything that went wrong. For instance, the echo-sounder was vital in locating fish and if it was out of action the success of the whole voyage would be threatened, and with it the crew's earnings, since they were linked to the catch.

The North Sea fishing grounds were in the beginning largely opened up by West Country fishermen, who made Hull their home port, one of the fore-runners of these being the Hellyer family. The St Andrew Dock (named after the patron saint of fishermen) in Hull was opened in 1883. The first vessels were smacks, but by the turn of the century these had been largely replaced by steam trawlers. Until the 1920s there was no form of communication by wireless, and when a trawler left port its whereabouts would remain unknown, unless it was reported by some other vessel on its return to port. The earliest communications at sea were by lamp signals to lighthouses, who reported to Lloyds, etc.

109. The steam trawler *Columbia*. The mark-boat of Messrs. Hellyer's Fishing Fleet.
(Photograph: Hull Daily Mail)

THE FIRST FITTINGS

Deep-sea trawlers sailed from all round the United Kingdom – Hull, Grimsby, Lowestoft, Swansea, Milford Haven, Fleetwood, Aberdeen and the Tyne being the biggest ports. Hull and Grimsby had the largest concentrations, and there was always great rivalry between them. Of course, there were also great numbers of smaller craft fishing in the North Sea, on the Westerly Grounds, and the Faroes, but these in general did not carry Radio Officers, relying on radio-telephony when it became available.

Now this once thriving industry is but a shadow of its former self, as the largely empty fish-docks in Hull and Grimsby mutely testify. Only museums remain to remind us of the prosperous times that have vanished, never to return, except that is, when our hearing is assailed by radio or TV with dismal reports of declining fish stocks.

It was not until the early 20s that fishing vessels began to be fitted with wireless telegraphy and it was interesting to the author, whose home is in Swansea, to discover that a local firm, Castle Trawlers, rented equipment from the Marconi Company as long ago as 1923. An even earlier fitting was on the Hull trawler *Columbia,* owned by Hellyers, pre-1920. But it was a further ten years before radio-telephony sets became the norm on deep-sea trawlers.

TRAWLER WORKING

The trawlers evolved their own highly specialised methods of communication, designed to enable vessels belonging to the same fleet owner to exchange mutually helpful information without it being picked up by rivals. At the same time they endeavoured to eavesdrop on the latter to find out what messages they were sending to their owners, and perhaps reveal if they had discovered a good fishing location. To do this effectively, the Radio Officer had to have at his fingertips a whole range of specialised data which could only be accumulated by experience. It demanded a comprehensive knowledge of the names and locations of the different fishing grounds, and the ability to have at instant recall the names, call signs and owners of other trawlers who might be in the vicinity.

That art, for that is what it was, became increasingly refined as the participants invented secret codes and phrases, which they constantly altered in their efforts to keep ahead of the game. Radio Officers became adept in

110 & 111. The fish dock, Hull, in the early 1930s.
(Photographs: E. A. Drewery)

memorising the voices of different skippers and Radio Officers, and since telegraphy still played an important role, recognising the Morse style of other Radio Officers.

Skill with the direction-finder was of great importance, so that a quick yet accurate bearing could be taken of a rival trawler who had perhaps radioed his owner or another vessel belonging to the same fleet, to say that he had discovered a good fishing ground.

At first the trawler owners only dimly realised the possibilities offered by wireless telegraphy. Radio Officers were available on hire from the Marconi Company, but typically, with the commercial acumen which had laid the foundation of their businesses they found a cheaper alternative. A fully qualified deep-sea Radio Officer earned about £3.00 per week and the hiring fee from the Marconi Company would just about double that. Their alternative was to create a new category of employee – the 'Deck-Hand Learner/Radio Operator'. Youths would be paid ten shillings a week and their keep for a specified period so that they could obtain the Postmaster General's 'Special' Certificate, which was a lesser qualification, and consequently came much cheaper. In this context it should be noted that it took at least three years' experience at sea on a trawler for a deck-hand to become qualified.

The author is indebted to her old friend and colleague, Mr E. A. Drewery, now retired in Hornsea, who went to sea in 1931, as one of the first of such

112. E. A. Drewery, early 1930s.
(Photograph: E. A. Drewery)

'learners', for his account of the progress of wireless telegraphy and electronics generally, on trawlers from the first days of its inception, and his life has encapsulated that history. In later years he obtained superior qualifications and was appointed to the shore staff of the Marconi Company in Hull, where he ended his career in the capacity of Desk Inspector. He was for a period manager of the company's offices in Karachi, Pakistan, but in the end chose to return to his home town of Hull rather than accept promotion elsewhere.

After completing his training he joined the steam trawler *Cape Sparvento* GTRK on 19th March 1931. It is interesting to note that seventy years later, Mr Drewery cannot mention the name of a trawler without automatically quoting its call sign, a characteristic that the author has noticed in talking to other Radio Officers who have served on trawlers.

In the second batch of learners there was a friend of his, the late A. S. Bryant, who went on to become one of Hull's best known and successful skippers – the only one to realise the trawler owner's dream of a Skipper/ Radio Operator.

A grateful tribute must be paid to Mr Harry Hutson of Cleethorpes, whose comprehensive work *Sparks on the Bridge* forms essential reading for anyone interested in radio on trawlers.

The first trawlers to be fitted with radio had of course been built without a radio cabin, and all kinds of odd corners had to be utilised; often by stripping out cupboards or even potato lockers. Sometimes a special 'cabin' was even welded on to the top of the galley aft.

Eventually, when a radio cabin came to be built into a new trawler, it would be a tiny affair usually on the after side of the bridge, perhaps only measuring as little as five by ten feet.

Betting messages were often sent by the crew, based on runners illegally copied down by the Radio Officer from Press Broadcasts. Occasionally, the Skipper and Radio Officer would run a book between them, sometimes with unfortunate results. If that happened, the Skipper would shout down to the crew on deck: 'Save them all; even the little ones!'

The various trawling owners had their own codes, which were changed every month. This was because the crew might sign off and join a ship owned by a rival company, and taking the code with him. On the fishing grounds, where there might be half a dozen or more of the same company's vessels trawling, they would report to their owner by wireless telegraphy, using these codes. One ship would be appointed as the organiser and call up his colleagues on the other company ships, using only the last

113. A trawler bridge, 1930s.
(Photograph: E. A. Drewery)

two letters of their call sign, while rivals did their best to guess what was being sent.

CONDITIONS OF SERVICE

The minimum requirement for a Radio Officer on a trawler was the PMG 'Special Certificate', but many possessed at least a 2nd Class Certificate, or even a 1st, and equally could well have been sailing deep-sea, and there were substantial compensations for the arduous conditions on trawlers. One was that voyages were rarely longer than three weeks at a time, whereas Radio Officers sailing deep-sea had to sign two year Articles and could often be away from their home and family for the whole of that period. For instance, Radio Officers employed by Marconi Marine on ships calling at an Indian port might very well find themselves ordered to sign off their ship and transfer to another vessel which might be on the Indian Coast trade for two years. In addition, Radio Officers on trawlers could expect to earn a bonus linked to the catch, and their take-home pay was usually more than they could earn deep-sea.

Radio Officers were employed in various ways – some directly by the trawler owners; others by the marine wireless companies who hired them out, along with the equipment. These were Marconi Marine, Siemens, Redifon, and the International Marine Radio Communication Company Ltd. Of these, Marconi Marine employed the largest number, probably more than all the others put together.

Most, though not all, were members of the Radio Officer's Union, and many stayed with the same Skipper, often for years, moving with him from ship to ship.

The average length of a fishing voyage in an Arctic trawler was about three weeks, and during that period it was a seven-day occupation with no extra payment for unsocial hours or overtime.

Steaming up to the main fishing grounds: Iceland, Bear Island, or the Barentz Sea, was known as 'Running Off'. Although the usual length of a voyage was about three weeks, there was a factor known as 'Gaffer's Time', which added a day to the voyage and thus reduced the daily earnings of the vessel. While this suited the owners, it did not matter to the crew, whose pay was made up of a weekly wage, 'Poundage' (roughly £6.00 per £1,000 gross of the catch landed) and 'Liver-Boiling' money.

An average pre-war crew was 14-16 men, but post-war this increased to twenty-one men, including a Skipper, Mate, Bosun, Third Hand, Radio Officer,

Chief and Second Engineer, and two firemen. The Chief and his fireman, and the Second and his fireman worked six hours on and six hours off. The cook and galley boy normally worked daylight hours, but during fishing, when operations were round the clock, warm drinks and food had to be provided during the night.

Quite a number of trawler Radio Officers had first gone to sea as cooks or deck-hands, and decided to improve their lot by taking the six month training course for a 'Special' Certificate offered by the technical colleges at Hull and Grimsby.

Sometimes a Radio Officer might be required to work as many as a hundred hours a week; there were no Bank Holidays, and it was not until the 1960s that the Humber trawler owners set up a voluntary pension scheme.

Skippers and Mates were not paid a wage; their earnings were related to a percentage of the catch, which they had negotiated each year with their employers. And in that and also the broader sense they were in the hands of the owners. Striking was a theoretical possibility but that would almost certainly be followed by black-listing, and resignation offered just as dismal a prospect. The crews were signed on and off on a voyage basis, and there was no obligation for a trawler owner to re-engage any member of the crew. The big trawler-owning families in the Humber dominated the industry, controlling everything from catching the fish, selling it, and the entire supporting infrastructure of ship-repairing and ship-chandlering.

The trawler owners were shrewd and very hard businessmen, but they created a multi-million pound industry and gave employment to thousands of people. And it must be said that they dealt fairly with their employees; everybody knew exactly where they stood. For instance, Hellyers of Hull used to pay their crews by cheque, in an effort to frustrate the 'scroungers' who waited outside their offices on settling days. They founded a medical surgery on the fish-dock, run by a Doctor Burns, who is still remembered with gratitude by many retired veteran fishermen still living.

The trawler owners also had their own 'Fisherman's Supply Store', which made gear available at reasonable prices. And it is well-known that widows and orphans and families who encountered hard times through misfortune or illness were never left without support. Occasionally, the trawler owners found themselves at the receiving end of criticism over conditions on trawlers during TV interviews, and they were curiously reticent about their good works. As one old friend of the writer recently put it, whatever their shortcomings they were great men of their time, and they and the type they fostered seem to have gone for ever, and the country is the poorer for their passing.

Some Radio Officers stayed with one skipper for years, moving from ship to ship with him. There was one case where a Radio Officer stayed on the same ship for twenty-three years, and he only left her when she went ashore in Iceland and became a total loss. Some successful skippers would transfer to a newly-built trawler and take their entire crew with them.

When the trawlers arrived in port to land their catch, the crew, after three weeks at sea, would always be anxious to get home as soon as possible to spend time with their families or girl friends. The average time in port between voyages was thirty-six hours, and if a crew member wanted to return to the same vessel, the only extended break he might get was when his ship went on her annual survey.

When the crew had left the trawler the skipper would report to his owner's office with details of the catch, and then a specialised team of dock workers would unload the fish and weigh it into kits of ten stone, ready to be auctioned in the fish market. During the 30s and later, particularly on the Dogger Bank and off Norway, the fish was gutted and boxed in ice in what was known as the 'Boxing Fleet', in which the Radio Officers played an important part. Perhaps twenty or thirty trawlers would be working closely together, being co-ordinated by W/T, and their catch ferried back to port by a special vessel for the purpose. There it could be quickly unloaded and dispatched to the London market at Billingsgate while the ferrying vessel returned to the Boxing fleet with a fresh supply of empty boxes.

During the 60s, the author, under a different name, was Chairman of the Marine Wireless Employers Negotiations Committee, which was concerned with deep-sea trawlers as well as deep-sea ships, and as such was regularly engaged in the discussions on wages and conditions that took place between the employers (the trawler owners and radio companies) and the Radio Officer's Union.

These usually came around once a year and took place either in Hull or London, where the favourite venue of the trawler owners was the Russell Hotel. When the choice of the lunch venue lay with the author, it was always Simpsons on the Strand, famous for its steaks, and two kinds of special house brew: 'Harley Street' and 'Wimpole Street'. She well remembers travelling down to London from Hull in company with the well-known trawler owner, Mr Tom Boyd (senior), and Mr Freddie Grinter, then the local Area Manager of the Marconi Marine Company. Freddie always used to stress the advisability of ordering fish and chips on the train, and very good fish it was – probably caught on one of Mr Boyd's ships.

114 & 115. Getting the catch on board, early 1930s.
(Photographs: E. A. Drewery)

116. Sorting and handling the catch, early 1930s.
(Photograph: E. A. Drewery)

LIVER-BOILING

Working on deck on a trawler was back-breaking; standing in boarded-off sections of the fore-deck in thigh-boots, oilskins, and sou'westers at the mercy of the often huge waves that would come crashing down upon the deck.

As fish were landed on board they would be gutted and the livers removed for boiling to form the raw material for Cod Liver Oil. In fact, it was not only cod livers that went into the boiler; other livers such as haddock went in as well. The baskets of livers were then carried aft and

161

tipped into the boiler, a horrible job in a trawler which might be trying to stand on its head in a rough sea. If the weather was really bad it would have to be delayed until conditions improved. The smell was terrible, and the oil would saturate clothes and destroy rubber-lined gear. The rubber would boil away from the lining and it then ceased to be waterproof.

Liver-boiling had to be carried out according to certain prescribed rules. The livers were never allowed to stand in the baskets for any length of time; exposure to sunshine was deleterious, and could adversely affect the quality of the end product unless it was avoided. The Radio Officer, who was usually much involved in these operations, would hook one end of a net hook into the handle of a basket, and drag it to the Liver-house, which ran athwartships at the stern. The four stone baskets would have to be lifted over a step about fourteen inches high, and then tipped into one of perhaps four boilers, each of which could take six baskets. A heavy iron lid would be screwed down with five wing-bolts.

The steam heating would then be turned on full for about twenty minutes, and then reduced to a simmer for another twenty minutes. After about another twenty minutes, the higher of three vertically mounted taps on the front of the boiler would be turned to allow the oil to run out though a gauze filter tray, from where it was piped into storage tanks below deck. Next, the middle tap would be tentatively tried; if the oil flowed freely, all well and good, but sometimes a porridge-like liquid came out. If that happened, the bottom valve had to be opened to lower the level in the boiler until the residue, which was known as 'Foots', was below the level of that tap. This was released into the sea by opening a valve underneath the boiler. In bad weather this could be utilised to have a calming effect on the sea – a practical example of 'pouring oil on troubled waters'!

The cod liver oil produced on the Hull and Grimsby trawlers was seen as a threat by the Norwegians, who had been the main producers until the British began to try and capture the market.

Members of the crew, including the Radio Officer, who were engaged in this task, were paid liver-boiling money which, to put it mildly, was hard-earned. During the 60s, when the author was, among other things, responsible for the sea and shore staff of the Marconi Marine Company, the company employed over 2,500 Radio Officers deep-sea and about 450 on deep-sea trawlers. Each one of these had a card on which were recorded details of what vessels the individual had served on, the periods concerned, leave earned, and so on.

Thirty years later, when researching for this book, these cards – then in the Marconi Museum at Chelmsford – came once more into their own. The Marconi Company Archivist, Miss Louise Weymouth, to whom the author takes this opportunity of acknowledging her extreme indebtedness, mentioned that enquiries were still being received in respect of the trawler cards. Apparently, claims by long retired Radio Officers for damage to their health sustained on trawlers, and particularly as a result of liver-boiling, were still the subject of claims for health compensation, in the same way as coalminers who had contracted emphysema. And the continued availability of these cards were enough in some cases to provide evidence of service which decided a claim in their favour.

BLACK FROST AND BLACK ICE – NIGHTMARE ON BEAR ISLAND

The Greenland Seas are, to say the least, a hostile environment, and the bad weather and heavy seas were made worse by the horrible phenomenon of Black Ice. Ice would form on the deck, superstructure, masts and rigging, and sometimes accumulated so rapidly and to such an extent that the vessel would be in danger of capsizing due to its weight. Somehow the crew would have to manage, in freezing conditions, to chop the ice clear in temperatures where as the fish were landed they froze solid.

Black Frost was an unpleasant corollary; even in fine weather it could suddenly come swirling down; the temperature would abruptly drop until everything on the vessel turned white, including men's whiskers. Freshly caught fish, wriggling as they came aboard, would be stiff as boards before they hit the deck.

If one had to pick an example of the extreme dangers that the Arctic trawlers had to face, it would be that of the steam trawler *St Sebastian*, owned by Thomas Hamling & Co. of Hull in late September 1938.

The disaster was recalled fifty years later in an article in the *Hull Daily Mail* by Christopher West who had been a deck-hand on the steam trawler *Davy*, which sailed from St Andrews Dock on 24th September 1938. Bear Island is a remote and desolate piece of land halfway between the northern tip of Norway and the Spitzbergen group of islands to the north. It was uninhabited except for the staff of a small Norwegian wireless station, and its highest mountain was known as 'Mount Misery'.

On the 30th of September the *Davy* had reached the vicinity of Bear Island, which is an important area for cod and codlings. The crew saw distress rockets being fired from the direction of the island, and then learned by radio that the *San Sebastian* had gone ashore there.

The Skipper, Albert Wilson, steamed his vessel around to the leeward side of the island, in company with another trawler, the *Cape Dunver*. Ten of the fittest and toughest members of the two crews landed and made their way to the site of the stricken ship. At first only the mast and funnel of the *St Sebastian* could be seen, but when the weather moderated and the tide was lower Skipper Wilson and the Master of the Norwegian salvage vessel *Jason*, which had then arrived on the scene, were able to clamber on board.

No survivors were to be seen on the nearby shore, but there were two bodies in the wheelhouse. Another ship which had arrived in the vicinity, the *Loch Oskaig*, later reported that a man had been sighted climbing over the rocks close to the wreck. However, by the time a rescue party from the wireless station reached that part of the coast, no trace of the man could be found. The two bodies in the wheelhouse were identified as Thomas Griffen, the cook, and Leonard O'Pray, a deck-hand, and one of the youngest on board. It was concluded that both had been drowned by heavy seas crashing into the wheelhouse. A total of sixteen lives were lost in the tragedy, including the Radio Officer, F. W. Keats of Hull.

WORLD WAR II

By 1939 the Royal Navy had begun requisitioning trawlers for use as patrol vessels and mine-sweepers. Fishing had to go on in spite of the war; it provided a much needed food source, and the trawlers had to be escorted to whatever extent the much-stretched resources of the Navy permitted. The losses of trawlers were tragically heavy – almost one for every week of the war being one estimate. On average about half the crews lost their lives.

THE LOSS OF THE TRAWLER *HOWE*. ONE OF THE GREAT
RESCUES IN MARITIME HISTORY

On 13th November 1931, ominously, the steam trawler *Howe*, owned by William Grant & Son of Grimsby, left her home port bound for the Arctic fishing grounds. Built by Cook, Welton & Gemmell of Beverley the previous year, she was the pride of the Grimsby fishing fleet.

Storm force seas, and possibly a navigational miscalculation (Skipper

George McGregor was subsequently completely exonerated), drove the ship ashore on the rock-bound coast of Bear Island, 500 miles within the Arctic Circle and 3,000 miles from home.

The amazing rescue of the crew forms a dramatic example of how wireless at sea came to the rescue of souls who otherwise would surely have perished. And this case particularly highlights how the Radio Officers on the trawlers all worked together, night and day, with calm efficiency and dedication to their work.

Huge seas drove the *Howe* still further onto the rocks where she became jammed. Most of the crew were in the forecastle when this occurred at 3.45 a.m. on 19th November. One by one they managed to scramble to the bridge, where sub-zero temperatures, biting winds and freezing spray made conditions almost unbearable. Fortunately, one of them had managed to grab a few tins of corned beef and a little bread, and that had to sustain them for the next few days.

The Radio Officer, Samuel Turner, sent out a distress message which was picked up by the Norwegian radio station at the north of Bear Island, who immediately re-broadcast it, alerting all the other vessels fishing in the area. It is difficult at this distance of time to say for certain how many ships turned up to help – contemporary estimates vary from twenty-six to more than a hundred.

The trawlers *Cape Spartivento*, *Elf King* and *Pennine* were the first ships to arrive at the eastern anchorage, near the Norwegian Wireless Station on the island. The Hull trawler *Imperialist*, Skipper 'Snowy' Worthington, re-mained on the western side.

'Snowy' Worthington tried without success to get a line across to the men on the *Howe*. One of the crew of the *Imperialist*, George Smith, who was later presented with the Sea Gallantry Medal by King George V, tried with another man to float across on a raft made out of cod liver oil containers. Realising that the task was impossible, the *Imperialist* and several other trawlers, including the *Elf King*, Skipper Ernest Drinkall, steamed around to the other side of the island and began putting men ashore.

Dozens of volunteers from the various crews set out to cover the eleven miles to the scene of the *Howe*'s position, laden with rescue gear. Despite the intense cold and being faced with only two hours of twilight each day the rescuers struggled on, mostly in the dark, led by a Norwegian called Johansen from the radio station. Fifty-eight hours after the *Howe* had gone ashore, they sighted it, gradually beginning to break up at the foot of the cliff. A line was lowered to the *Howe* where it was picked up, and the crew eventually hauled up one at a time on a home-made Breeches Buoy, constructed on the orders of Skipper McGregor of the *Howe*.

Once ashore, they had to struggle back to the north side of the island, where food and shelter was awaiting them at the radio station. Unconfirmed reports later said that the *Howe* broke up completely within a few hours of the crew being taken off. Their rescue had been truly miraculous.

The contribution made by wireless to the rescue was absolutely vital. During the last few hours that the *Howe*'s wireless was still working its position had been accurately determined by radio bearings taken by the Radio Officers on the *Imperialist* and *Elf King*. And when it had become necessary to land more men to help with the rescue operation, it was the CQ call sent out by Radio Officer Scott on the *Pennine* that brought help from other ships, who were enabled to home in on the anchorage with the aid of radio bearings provided by Radio Officer Drewery.

But some good things came out of the disaster; a warning marker was placed on Bear Island to alert trawlers fishing in those rich but dangerous grounds, and many more trawlers came to be fitted with wireless, as more and more trawler owners came to appreciate its importance.

Appendices

1. A basic technical description of the first spark transmitters and receivers (with circuit drawings).

2. A pioneer voyage – the *Lake Champlain*, 1901.

3. The *Cunard Daily Bulletin* – the first ship's newspaper.

4. A North Atlantic communication chart issued by the Marconi International Marine Communication Company Ltd.

5. Early radio-telegram charges.

6. The prospectus of the Marconi Wireless Telegraph Company Ltd., 1908.

7. Report of the Directors of the Marconi Wireless Telegraph Company Ltd., 1908.

8. A Rival Bid.

9. Letter addressed by the Marconi Wireless Telegraph Company Ltd. to its shareholders, 12th October 1909, following the mandatory acquisition of the company's shore stations by the Postmaster-General.

10. List of awards for gallantry to Marconi Radio Officers during World War II.

11. Typical wireless cabins over the years (1 to 10).

A Basic Technical Description of the first Spark Transmitters and Receivers (with circuit drawings)

A DETAILED TECHNICAL DESCRIPTION would be out of place in this book, but some degree of basic information seems called for if only to guide the reader through what might otherwise be confusing references to the pieces of early equipment that have to be mentioned. But even to a technically-minded generation familiar with solid state devices and the world of micro-chips, a simple description of the elegant early solutions to the problem of producing electro-magnetic waves might be interesting, rather in a same way that a vintage car enthusiast likes to follow the work of pioneers like Daimler-Benz or Henry Ford.

The author has not been able to resist the temptation of nostalgically recalling the *Admiralty Handbooks of Wireless Telegraphy*, Volumes I and II, from which she and the rest of her generation first imbibed the principles of radio theory (see page 57). As well as being of excellent content and crystal clear, they are period pieces, replete with references to mysterious items such as L.F.I.C.I.'s (Low Frequency Iron Cored Inductances) and units of electrical capacity measured in 'Jars'. Capacitors were referred to as 'condensers', a perfectly apt description of the early devices of that name. These consisted of glass jars coated on both sides with metal foil. Leyden Jars, as they were called, created, with stunning simplicity, the necessary two electrical plates, separated by an insulating dielectric

It is extraordinary how these terms, which reek of Victorian laboratories, Bunsen burners, brass terminals and polished mahogany, still linger distinctly in the memory, along with Carbon Filament Lamps, 'Back EMF', and Tuning Jiggers.

BASIC TRANSMITTER AND COHERER RECEIVER

At the heart of the early transmitters lay an induction coil which provided a means of generating high voltages. A current passing through a wire produces a varying electro-magnetic field, and if two coils are wound on the same former and an interrupted current passed through the first (primary) winding, a current will be induced in the secondary winding. If the secondary winding has twice the number of turns as the primary, twice the voltage will appear across it, i.e. it has been stepped up. (It can be stepped down if the process is reversed.)

Basically, Marconi's first transmitter consisted of nothing more or less than this; the high voltage being applied to two small brass spheres, where it jumped across the gap, producing a spark. Marconi's great idea was to connect each sphere to a square metal radiating surface. Then followed his big break-through, which was to place one plate as high as possible above

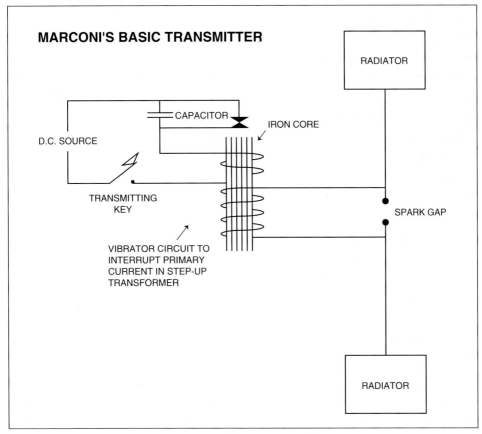

Fig. 1. Marconi's Basic Transmitter.

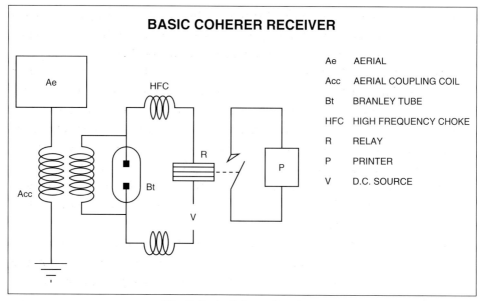

BASIC COHERER RECEIVER

Ae	AERIAL
Acc	AERIAL COUPLING COIL
Bt	BRANLEY TUBE
HFC	HIGH FREQUENCY CHOKE
R	RELAY
P	PRINTER
V	D.C. SOURCE

Fig. 2. Basic Coherer Receiver.

the ground and connect the other to earth, the latter acting as the bottom plate. Current in the primary winding was interrupted by a simple vibrating contact mechanism such as used in the common electric bell, and a Morse key could be used to break the transmission and convey information.

Marconi's basic transmitter produced a spark of very short duration, which energised an oscillatory circuit consisting of the transmitter inductance coil L1 in Fig. 4). The duration of the oscillation was damped (shortened) because the spark gap offered a high resistance to alternating currents. Figure 5 shows an improved arrangement where the stepped-up voltage is applied directly across a capacitor. When the spark occurs, the capacitor discharges through the circuit inductance (coils L1 and L2). Oscillations are set up in the aerial circuit L3 and L4, and because of the presence of the inductive coupling, they are not so highly damped. This has the advantage that the aerial can be tuned by L4.

THE QUENCH GAP

Marconi improved his original spark gap by introducing the quench gap, which consisted of a number of small gaps formed by metal plates separated by mica insulators in series (in line). The distance between the plates was very small, so that the sparks were also small. Because the metal plates were larger and cooled by radiating fins the air between them did not become so heated, and consequently ionised. This allowed a much higher spark frequency, which in turn produced a clearer note at the receiver.

The receiver utilised a device known as a Branly coherer. This basically consisted of a small glass tube containing metal filings whose electrical resistance changed when subjected to an electro-magnetic wave because they became more tightly packed (cohered). The device was named after the Frenchman who discovered it. When the electro-magnetic wave was withdrawn the filings de-cohered, a process which could be speeded up by tapping the glass lightly.

The change in current produced by the coherer could be used to work a small relay which in turn was connected to a Morse printer. Later, the device was refined by arranging an electric bell-like gong to lightly tap the coherer tube.

THE MAGNETIC DETECTOR

The basic coherer system was not very reliable and inherently reduced the speed of signalling because of the time taken for the Branly tube to de-cohere. Sir Ernest Rutherford had shown in the 1890s that a magnetised steel needle could be de-magnetised by an electro-magnetic field produced by a spark discharge. In 1902 Marconi patented his Magnetic Detector, which is elegant in the simplicity of its concept (see Fig. 3).

A continuous band of insulated iron wire is slowly rotated by two wooden pulleys and passes through a glass tube between the poles of two horseshoe magnets. A coil of wire was wound around the glass tube and connected to the aerial and the earth. A second coil is wound over the first, to which it becomes inductively connected, which feeds a pair of telephone earpieces.

The iron wire becomes partially magnetised within the glass tube, and when a signal appears in the primary (aerial) coil the magnetic field changes, producing a current in the second coil, and consequently a sound in the telephone earpieces. The system possessed the enormous advantage that decohering ceases to be such a problem and much higher signalling speeds immediately became possible. The system was also more mechanically robust and became the standard receiver at sea (and elsewhere) for many years, until it was superseded by thermionic valve receivers.

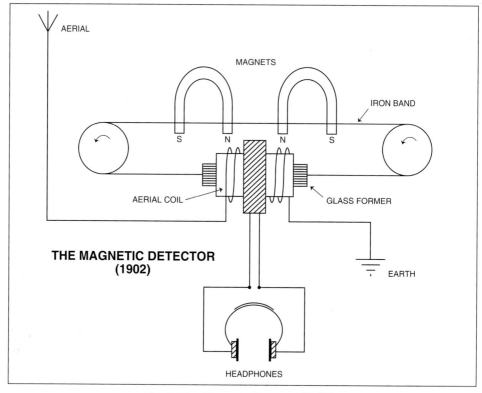

Fig. 3. The Magnetic Detector (1902).

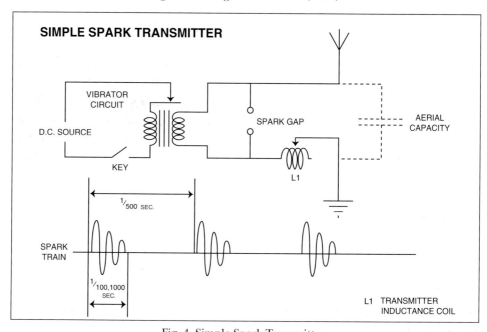

Fig. 4. Simple Spark Transmitter.

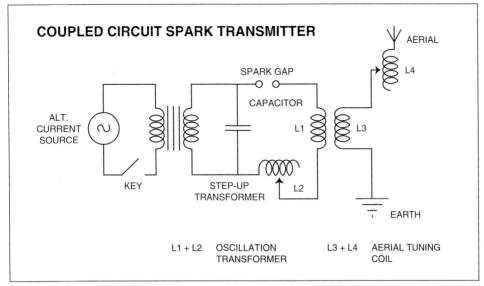

Fig. 5. Coupled Circuit Spark Transmitter.

Marconi's spark discharger produced an almost continuous wave, which could not be recognised by the Magnetic Detector, and this led to the introduction of a disc discharger to the transmitter.

THE DISC DISCHARGER (see Fig. 6)

A disc fitted with copper studs was rotated at a high speed, which interrupted the spark at a frequency dictated by the speed of rotation and the number of studs. The high voltage required was obtained from a single phase alternator whose output was applied to the primary of a suitable step-up transformer. The alternator was fitted with up to twelve pairs of poles and the discharging disc was keyed on to the same shaft. The disc, which was suitably insulated from the shaft, had a heavy rim of brass or copper, and studs of the same material equal in number to the alternator poles, and fitted at equal distances around it.

When the disc rotated it passed two copper spark electrodes which were placed so that they were opposite two adjacent studs at the moment the voltage reached its peak in each half cycle. The position of the two electrodes were adjustable in relation to the rotation of the disc in order to achieve synchronisation. When the transmitting key was pressed, allowing a current to flow through the primary of the step-up transformer, the neces-

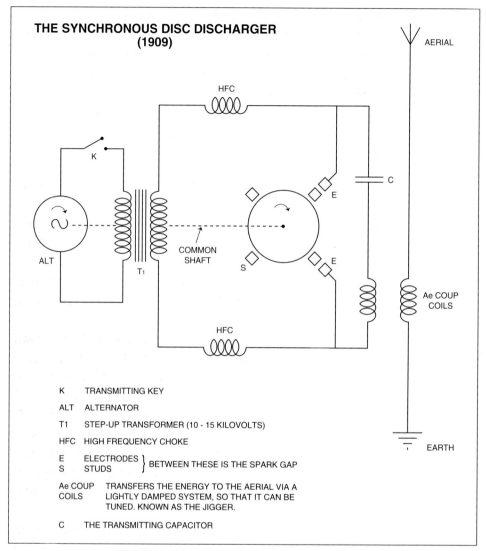

THE SYNCHRONOUS DISC DISCHARGER (1909)

K	TRANSMITTING KEY
ALT	ALTERNATOR
T1	STEP-UP TRANSFORMER (10 - 15 KILOVOLTS)
HFC	HIGH FREQUENCY CHOKE
E	ELECTRODES
S	STUDS } BETWEEN THESE IS THE SPARK GAP
Ae COUP COILS	TRANSFERS THE ENERGY TO THE AERIAL VIA A LIGHTLY DAMPED SYSTEM, SO THAT IT CAN BE TUNED. KNOWN AS THE JIGGER.
C	THE TRANSMITTING CAPACITOR

Fig. 6. The Synchronous Disc Discharger (1909).

sary high voltage was applied to a capacitor connected in series with a coupling coil, and charged it up. At the peak voltage the spark jumped across the two gaps between the electrodes and discharged the capacitor, which in turn generated a series of oscillations in the aerial and excited the aerial.

The oscillations occurred in the aerial at its natural frequency (dictated by its dimensions) because the tuned aerial was only slightly damped. The aerial coils were wound on an ebonite former with various tappings to enable tuning to be carried out and the whole assembly was known as the transmitting jigger. The transmitting capacitor was a somewhat massive affair consisting of thirty-four glass plates interleaved with zinc sheets and contained within a galvanised iron framework. The alternate zinc sheets were connected together and each set brought out to an insulated terminal fixed on top of the lead-lined teak box that housed the whole assembly.

The dots and dashes produced by the operation of the Morse key could be heard in the receiving head telephones as musical notes at twice the frequency of the alternator.

By the early 1920s, when the problem of sealing glass to copper had been overcome, thermionic valves could be used to produce a continuous amplitude transmission wave, which could be rectified at the receiving end, producing the necessary rectified signals which could be heard in the receiving telephone headset.

Before leaving this very elementary introduction to technical basics, a brief description of the principle of the Thermionic Valve might not be out of place.

A Thermionic Valve fundamentally consists of an exhausted glass envelope containing three elements: a Cathode, which when supplied with an electric current emits electrons, which are negatively charged. These are attracted to the Anode Plate, which is positively charged from an external source. In between the two is placed a Grid, and if a varying voltage is applied to it the flow of electrons to the plate will be correspondingly affected, causing a change in voltage at the anode. A changing voltage at the anode therefore appears, driven by the changing voltage at the grid, and greatly amplified, to a degree depending on the valve design and level of voltages applied to it.

By attaching suitable circuitry which links the changing voltage at the anode and feeds it back to the grid, a self-oscillatory circuit can be produced which lends itself ideally to generating a continuous wave, which can be amplified and used as a transmitter.

Equally, as a receiver the Triode Valve, as it became known, was admirably suited to detecting received radio signals which were applied to the grid.

APPENDIX 2

A Pioneer Voyage

RECOLLECTIONS OF THE FIRST BRITISH OPERATOR
TO MAKE A TRANSATLANTIC CROSSING

By F. S. STACEY

(An article in the *Wireless World*, June 1917)

IN RESPONDING TO THE INVITATION of the Editor to place on record a few notes regarding my pioneer voyage on the s.s. *Lake Champlain*, I am faced with the fact that no less than sixteen years have elapsed since this interesting event occurred. My memory, however, is still fresh upon many points which may be of interest to those operators who are now sailing the seas with apparatus of modern type. It will be seen later on that the conditions under which we had to work at that time were very different from those prevailing today.

It was in the year 1899 that I joined the Marconi Company, and after having made myself familiar with the apparatus, which was of a comparatively simple nature, at the office of the Company, then at 28 Mark Lane, and later on at Chelmsford, under Dr. Murray, I was able to act as technical assistant at several important demonstrations. When the Belgian mail packet *Princess Clementine* was fitted with wireless telegraphy I served aboard as operator.

The *Princess Clementine* having proved successfully that wireless telegraphy was a reliable form of communication, Captain C. V. Daly, who had then recently joined the Marconi Company as Marine Superintendent, arranged with the Beaver Line to install a set of apparatus on board the s.s. *Lake Champlain*. The arrangements were made with a Mr Jones, later known as Sir Alfred Jones, and one of the directors of Messrs Elder, Dempster and Company. Considerable importance was attached to the venture, particularly as the *Lake Champlain* was one of the Beaver Line's new vessels. As soon as negotiations were concluded I was instructed to get together the necessary apparatus and proceed to Liverpool to join the vessel, which was lying in the Alexandra Dock. The work of installation was carried out under the supervision of the late Mr Bullock, afterwards appointed Traffic Manager to the Marconi International Marine Communication Company Limited.

The transmitting apparatus consisted of a ten-inch induction coil working off current supplied by two six-volt accumulators. Four six-volt accumulators were supplied, two being worked whilst the other two were on charge. At that time there was no switchboard for charging, and the mains were connected to the accumulator; through a bank of six carbon filament lamps which provided the necessary resistance. There were no tuning circuits, transmitting jiggers or aerial tuning inductances, the aerial being simply connected to one side of the spark gap and the 'earth' to the other. A three-centimetre spark was used between balls of 1½ centimetres diameter. The receiving apparatus consisted of two coherer receivers with a Morse inker, the signals being received on tape. The aerial consisted of two wires supported about one hundred feet above the waterline by means of a sprit, hoisted to the top of the mast and about twelve feet long. These wires, which were made of 7/20 I.R.V.B. electric lighting cable, were kept six feet apart by means of two spreaders, one at the top and one at the bottom. The aerial was led into the wireless cabin by a Bradfield insulator practically identical in form with that used at the present day. The transmitting key consisted of a switch and key combined. The lever had at one end an ebonite handle and a platinum contact, and this worked upon another contact beneath. At the opposite end of the lever was attached a length of ebonite fitted with another contact and a terminal. When the key was 'up' this back contact rested upon a lower contact connected to the receiving instruments by means of a length of lead-covered cable, the lead covering of which was very carefully earthed. The terminal attached to the contact on the ebonite extension was connected with the aerial lead, so that when the key was at rest the receiver was directly connected with the aerial. Thus, when receiving, electrical oscillations collected by the aerial wire passed to the terminal on the top of the ebonite rod extension on the key, from there to the contact and thence by the lead-covered cable to the receiver. On depressing the key for signalling the contacts at the end of the ebonite rod were broken and the receiver cut out.

As there was no available accommodation on the boat for the wireless apparatus, a special cabin had to be built, and it is interesting to compare this with the specially designed and equipped cabins used at the present day. It consisted of little more than a cupboard 4 ft. 6 in. in length and

3 ft. 6 in. in width, one side being formed by the iron bulkhead. It was made of matchboarding, without any windows, and when natural light was required the door had to be opened. The total cost of this palatial structure was £5!

The apparatus itself was mounted on a table covered with green baize, the accumulators being placed on the floor and the lamp resistance for charging the cells screwed on to the wall. Two induction coils were supplied, one being used and the other being kept as a spare. The two coil boxes one on top of the other served as a seat, the empty coil boxes providing a convenient cupboard for spares and sundries. The stationery supply was of the simplest description, and consisted of P.V. forms, Post Office telegraph forms, and some of Marconi's wireless telegraph forms printed in red. Traffic abstracts and the many other papers now in use had then not come into being.

The s.s. *Lake Champlain* sailed on 21st of May 1901, with about 1,200 people on board. Soon after we cleared the land we established communication with the station at Holyhead (long since dismantled), and soon after losing touch with this we picked up Rosslare. Numerous messages were sent and received to and from the owners; messages were also sent by members of the crew. Our busy time soon ceased, however, for there were no other stations to communicate with in Great Britain and none had been erected on the American side.

The new wireless installation naturally aroused tremendous curiosity and interest among the passengers and crew, who crowded in and out of our tiny cabin from morn till eve. It is safe to say that it was much harder work explaining the apparatus and satisfying the visitors than actually manipulating it when occasion required. When the ship arrived at Halifax it was invaded by an army of newspaper reporters, who were quick to realise the possibilities of the new method of communicating, and Captain Stewart, Chief Engineer Samson and the author were busy giving interviews and explaining the apparatus. Special articles appeared in the newspapers and were cabled to America and England. On arrival at Montreal further interviews were given and much interest aroused. Representatives from several of the scientific societies and technical colleges visited the ship, and Mr Keeley, at that time Government Inspector of Telegraphs, journeyed from Ottawa with the express purpose of examining the apparatus. As a result of his visit the Canadian Government cabled to England and ordered two sets of apparatus for communication across the Straits of Belle Isle, a distance of twenty-two miles, where considerable difficulty had been experienced in maintaining cable communication owing to the cable being continually felled by icebergs.

The return voyage was without event until on calling Crookhaven, which had not been erected at the time of our outward journey, but which was now working, we were considerably surprised to receive a call from the Cunarder s.s. *Lucania*, which was outward bound on her first trip with wireless. I exchanged several messages with the operator (Mr J. St. Vincent Pletts), and as soon as communication was finished I picked up Crookhaven. Telegrams were sent to the owners and to Queenstown, and received some hours before they would have been if the old methods of signalling by means of flags had been used. After leaving Queenstown we communicated with Rosslare and Holyhead, and in due course arrived at Liverpool.

The 'Cunard Daily Bulletin'

(Courtesy David Evans)

Cunard Daily Bulletin.

R.M.S. "LUCANIA."   TUESDAY, JULY 19, 1904.   [PRICE 2½d. OR 5 CENTS.

In the article which alludes to the Cunard Line exhibits at St. Louis, there appears a view of the 21,000 ton twinscrew steamer "Caronia," which is now completing at the works of Messrs. Brown, the eminent Clydebank shipbuilders. This magnificent steamer was launched on the 13th July under peculiarly happy auspices, the launching ceremony being gracefully performed by Mrs. J. S. Choate, wife of the distinguished United States Ambassador in Great Britain. The "Caronia" is probably the heaviest ship ever launched from a slipway, her launching weight being 13,500 tons. Her great size is rendered apparent by the following figures :—

Length	..	676 ft. 0 in.
Breadth	..	72 ft. 6 in.
Depth to Boat Deck	..	80 ft. 0 in.
Gross Tonnage	..	21,000
Passengers	..	2,650
Crew	..	450

The passenger quarters for all classes will be exceptionally fine, and all the third class will be carried in two or four berthed rooms. The first class smoke room will have an open fire place in hammered copper, and the drawing room one of exquisite elegance in *fluer de rose* marble. There will also be a number of family suites of rooms, consisting of parlours, bed and bath rooms, &c. The aim of owners and builders has been the production of a strong, safe and splendidly appointed vessel, and they have succeeded admirably. After the launch Mr. Choate echoed a general sentiment when he hoped that the "Caronia" and the other ships to be added to the Cunard Line would enrich the noble roll of frequent, happy and safe communication between Great Britain and the United States.

2   CUNARD DAILY BULLETIN.

The Cunard Line . . . .
at the . . .
St. Louis Exhibition. .

Visitors to the St. Louis Exhibition cannot fail to be struck with the exhibit palaces comprised in the Transportation section of this " Universal Exposition." Here locomotion in

s.s. "BRITANNIA," 1,154 Tons.

all its varying phases is strikingly illustrated. A special feature is made of marine exhibits, and in this connection there can be no more striking object lesson of advancement in naval architecture and shipowning enterprise than

s.s. "SCOTIA," 3,871 Tons.

that presented by the collection of models illustrating in epitome the progress and development of the Cunard Line. These models form a crystallised history of the Cunard

s.s "RUSSIA," 2,960 Tons

Steamship Company and bear striking testimony to the enterprise of the premier British ocean Transportation Company. Beginning with the

historic " BRITANNIA," which sailed on her first voyage on Independence Day, 1840, the visitor can trace the whole process of evolution from paddle to screw, from single screw to twin

s.s. "UMBRIA," 8,127 Tons.

screws, and on to the quadruple propellers of the 25-knot steamers. The early boats were of wood, then came iron, and lastly mild steel. Some of these models we illustrate pictorially. The "SCOTIA," built in 1862, was the last and finest of the paddle steamers and broke all records, steaming from Liverpool to New York in 8 days, 22 hours. A later upholder of Cunard prestige was the famous and handsome " RUSSIA," whose commander, Captain Cook, navigated her 630,000 miles without the

s.s. "CAMPANIA," 12,950 Tons.

slightest accident, the cabin passengers who sailed with him numbering no fewer than 26,076. The " UMBRIA " and " ETRURIA," the " CAMPANIA " and " LUCANIA " tell their own story of regular and speedy voyages and excellent accommodation for all classes of passengers, while the reputation of the huge sister-vessels " SAXONIA " and " IVERNIA," for steadiness in all conditions of weather is unique. The " CARONIA," 21,000 tons, and her sister, the

CUNARD DAILY BULLETIN. 3

"CARMANIA," which will be fitted with turbine engines, are other links in the chain of progress, while the Express Turbine Steamers will be unequalled in size and speed, and will represent all that is superlative in naval architecture, in marine engineering, and in luxurious hotel accommodation. Glance at the first model, that of the diminutive "BRITANNIA," in her day the finest ship afloat. Sixty-four years have elapsed since this pioneer Cunarder first cleaved American waters, and it is by comparing the first and latest vessel of

the "BRITANNIA," while along any one of their turbine-driven shafts will be transmitted five

s.s. "SAXONIA," 14,280 Tons.

or six times the total horse-power developed by the engines of the whole pioneer fleet of four

s.s. "CARONIA," 21,000 Tons (Building)

the line that it is possible to realize the vast progress which has been made. Each of these 25-knot steamers will be from 25 to 30 times the gross tonnage of the "BRITANNIA," and 85 to 90 times the power. Their turbine engines will

steamers. The adoption of rotary engines means increased speed for the same boiler power, due to reduced weight of machinery and increased economy in steam, an utter absence of all vibration, and hence, greater comfort, while

The 25 Knot TURBINE STEAMERS (Building)

enable the new flyers to make the voyage between Liverpool and New York in a little more than one-third of the time occupied by

the smaller engine room spaces and openings will ensure commodious passenger quarters and promenade spaces.

CUNARD DAILY BULLETIN.

MARCONIGRAMS

DIRECT TO THE SHIP.

EDITORIAL OFFICE,

R.M.S. "LUCANIA."

Monday, July 18th, 1904.

Received from the Marconi Station, Poldhu, (Cornwall), at 0.30 p.m.   Distance, 720 miles.

THE FAR EAST.

General Oku has made a startling indictment against the conduct of the Russian soldiers in the field.

THIBET.

General Macdonald's advance on Lhassa is being continued from Khotang, but with difficulty, owing to the wet weather.

Further resistance is expected at any moment.

CANADIAN NEWS.

An enthusiastic farewell demonstration was given to Lord Dundonald on his departure from Toronto on Saturday.

NAVAL INTELLIGENCE.

The British torpedo-boat destroyer "Haughty" was run down off Harwich yesterday, but fortunately no lives were lost.

WEATHER REPORT.

The weather in the English Channel remains fine, with strong easterly wind.

Monday, July 18th, 1904.   Midnight.

Latest News through Reuters Agency,

Received from the Marconi Station, Poldhu, (Cornwall).   Distance, 1000 miles.

WAR NEWS.

General Kuroki reports from headquarters that yesterday morning two divisions of the

STOP-PRESS.

Russians took advantage of a dense fog that prevailed at the time, and made a desperate attack upon the Japanese positions around Motienling between Liaoyang and Newchwang. The Japanese, however, offered a stubborn resistance, and repulsed the attack with but slight loss.

THE AMERICAN MEAT STRIKE.

At the conference between the American packers and the Executive Committee of the Butchers' Union no satisfactory terms could be agreed upon, and negotiations have now been broken off.   At present all chance of a settlement of the strike appears to have vanished.

A large crowd of persons who had been watching a ball game at Chicago to-day made a fierce attack upon four negro strike breakers who were coming from the stock yards.

As a result of the fight, two of the crowd were shot, a policeman stabbed, and one negro badly injured.

CUNARD DAILY BULLETIN.   5

RIVAL WIRELESS SYSTEMS.

THE USES OF DIPLOMACY.

At the suggestion of the Lighthouse Board, the New York Herald's wireless signal station on the Nantucket lightship, which hitherto has rendered splendid service, has been discontinued. Great hardship is thereby inflicted as regards the Atlantic liners which had been able to communicate news of their approaching arrival in America ten or eleven hours in advance, which was esteemed as a great advantage by the commercial community and by the relatives and friends of passengers. The Marconi system was employed, and this aroused the resentment of German competitors, who sought the assistance of the diplomatic service.

The story of the removal of the Marconi installation begins with a letter which the German Ambassador to the United States addressed to the Secretary of State at Washington. In his letter Baron Speck von Sternburg, acting under the direction of the Imperial Chancellor, called the attention of the American State Department to the fact that German vessels fitted with German wireless telegraph systems were precluded from communicating with the wireless station on the Nantucket shoal. "As far as is known to the Imperial Government," wrote the Ambassador, "the Marconi Company has no right in the United States of America to refuse to communicate with vessels by means of other systems."

The American Secretary of State, Mr. Cortelyou, then asked the Marconi Company to co-operate in receiving and transmitting messages written according to the German system of wireless telegraphy. The company replied that the difficulties were insuperable, and that the company was unable "to overturn its system and undo the work of years for sentimental reasons." The company also explained that all Transatlantic liners, including the German vessels, were equipped with Marconi wireless apparatus, and concluded: "The issue raised by the German Government is academic rather than real, and shows the intent of the German Emperor to attempt to effect through diplomatic channels what could not be accomplished in business competition."

This morning I interviewed a number of prominent shipping and commercial men on the subject. All deplored what they called the "dog in the manger" policy of the German competitors. The removal of the installation at Nantucket, they said, means not only commercial inconvenience, but increased danger to navigation.

FROM THE LOG.

July 17th, at 9 p.m., Lat. 50·46 N., Long. 14·30 W. In wireless communication with S.S. "Kaiser Wilhelm II," bound East.

July 17th, at 9 p.m., Lat. 50·46 N., Long. 14·30 W. Passed one mile north of a Dominion Line S.S., bound East.

July 18th, at 10.30 a.m. In wireless communication with the S.S. "La Bretagne" (French line), bound West.

July 18th, at 7.30 p.m. In wireless communication with R.M.S. "Carpathia," bound East.

THE DAY'S RUN.

Sunday, July 17th, Lat. 51·21 N., Long. 9·44 W.   61 miles from Daunts Rock.

Monday, July 18th, Lat. 49·29 N., Long. 23·16 W.   529 miles.

WEATHER.

Light to moderate S.E. winds, fine weather, with moderate S.E. sea.

"LEGAL METAMORPHOSES."

(From "Chambers' Journal," 1850.)

HE laughingly complied, and we arrived at the house arm-in-arm. We were admitted by an elderly woman, and there was a young man—a moustached clerk—seated at a desk in an inner room writing. He eyed me for a moment, but I gave him no opportunity for a distinct view of my features, and I presently handed M. Bellebon a card, on which I had contrived to write, unobserved, "Send away the clerk;" and, in answer to M. Bellebon's glance of enquiry, I merely said, "that, as I did not wish to be known there as a police officer, it was essential that the minute search I was about to make should be without witnesses." He agreed, and the woman was also sent away upon a distant errand. Every conceivable place did I ransack; every scrap of paper that had writing upon it I eagerly perused. At length the search was over, apparently without result.

"You are quite sure, Monsieur Bellebon, as you informed the superintendent, that Monsieur le Breton has no female relations in this country?"

"Positive," he replied. "I have made the most explicit enquiries both from the clerk, Dubarle, and of the woman servant."

Just then the clerk returned, out of breath with haste I noticed, and I took my leave without affording the young gentleman so clear a view of my face as he was evidently anxious to obtain.

"No female acquaintance," thought I, as I re-entered the private room of the tavern I had left an hour before. "From whom came, then, these scraps of perfumed note-paper I found in his desk, I wonder?" I sat down and endeavoured to piece them out; but, after considerable trouble, satisfied myself that they were parts of different notes written by one hand, and that hand a female one.

About two hours after this, I was sauntering along in the direction of Stoke-Newington, when a small discoloured handbill lying in a haberdasher's shop window, arrested my attention. It ran thus:—"Two guineas reward.—Lost, an Italian greyhound. The tip of its tail has been chopped off, and it answers to the name of Fidèle." Underneath the reader was told to "enquire within."

"Fidèle," I exclaimed; "Any relation to M. le Breton's fair correspondent's Fidèle, I wonder?" In a twinkling my pocket book was out, and I re-perused by the gaslight on one of the perfumed scraps the following portion of a sentence, "ma pauvre Fidèle est per." The bill, I observed, was dated nearly three weeks previously. I entered the shop and said I knew a person who had found such a dog as was there advertised for. The woman at the counter said she was glad to hear it, as the lady was much grieved at the animal's loss.

"What is the lady's name?" I asked.

"It is French, I believe; here it is with the address in the day book written by herself."

I eagerly read—"Madame Levasseur, Oak Cottage, about one mile on the road from Edmonton to Southgate." Here were the indications of a trail which might lead to success, and I determined to follow it up. I then hastened westward to a well-known dog-fancier, and procured the loan of an ugly Italian hound. The requisite loss of the tip of its tail was very speedily accomplished, and so quickly healed, that the newness of the excision could not be suspected. I arrived at the lady's residence about twelve o'clock on the following day, thoroughly disguised as a vagabond Cockney dog-dealer. The mistress of the Old Cottage was at home, but indisposed, and the servant said she would take the dog to her, though if I would take it out of the basket she herself could tell me if it was Fidèle or not. I replied that I would only show the dog to the lady, and would not trust it out of my hands. This message was carried upstairs, and after waiting some time outside, I was re-admitted, desired to wipe my shoes carefully, and to walk up. Madame Levasseur, a showy-looking woman, was seated on a sofa, in vehement expectation of embracing her dear Fidèle, and my vagabond appearance so startled her, that she screamed loudly for her husband, M. Levasseur. This gentleman, a fine, tall, whiskered, moustached person, hastened into the apartment, half-shaved, and with his razor in his hand.

"Qu'est ce qu'il y a donc?" he demanded.

To be continued.

CUNARD DAILY BULLETIN. 7

The 25 knot Express Turbine Steamers building will be the largest and fastest steamships in the world.

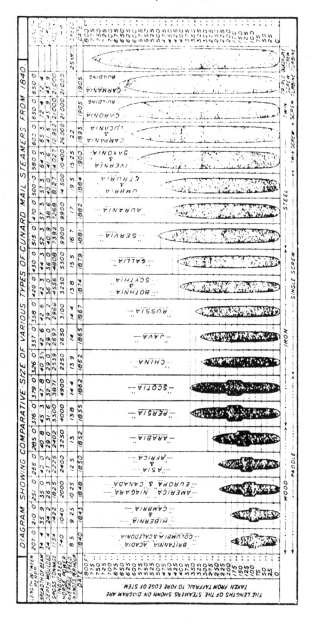

R.M.S. "LUCANIA."

DIMENSIONS—LENGTH, 620 FT.   BEAM, 65 FT. 3 INS.   12,952 TONS.   30,000 HORSE-POWER.

STAMP.

PROPOSED   SAILINGS.

LIVERPOOL NEW YORK SERVICE.				LIVERPOOL BOSTON SERVICE.			
FROM LIVERPOOL.			FROM NEW YORK.	FROM LIVERPOOL.			FROM BOSTON.
July 16. Sat.....	LUCANIA ..	July 30, Sat.		July 19, Tues...	IVERNIA	Aug. 2,	Tues.
July 23. Sat.....	UMBRIA	Aug. 6, Sat.		Aug. 2. Tues...	SAXONIA	Aug. 16,	Tues.
July 26. Tues. ..	CARPATHIA.	Aug. 9, Tues.		Aug. 9. Tues...	SYLVANIA	Aug. 23,	Tues.
July 30. Sat. ..	CAMPANIA ..	Aug. 13. Sat.		Aug. 16. Tues..	IVERNIA	Aug. 30,	Tues.
				Aug. 30. Tues...	SAXONIA......	Sept. 13,	Tues.
				Sept. 6, Tues...	SYLVANIA	Sept. 20,	Tues.

ADRIATIC,   MEDITERRANEAN,   NEW   YORK.

The "PANNONIA," "ULTONIA," and "SLAVONIA" are now running from New York to the Mediterranean, calling at Gibraltar, Naples, Palermo, Trieste and Fiume. Passengers by these Steamers may land at any of the ports named, and visit at leisure places of interest in Spain, France, Italy, Germany, Sicily, Austria or Hungary, continuing their journey overland to England; or, if they prefer to do so, they may remain in the ship all the time and return in her to New York ; or, as a third course, they may make a stay in any of the Countries named and rejoin a subsequent Cunard Mediterranean ship at any of her calling ports.

Whichever course be selected the traveller will be well repaid, for there is no round of travel in which so many interesting and beautiful places are found so near together as in the Mediterranean Sea.

THE "CAMPANIA" "LUCANIA," "ETRURIA," "UMBRIA," "IVERNIA," "SAXONIA," "AURANIA," "CARPATHIA," "SLAVONIA" AND "PANNONIA" ARE FITTED WITH MARCONI'S SYSTEM OF WIRELESS TELEGRAPHY.

LUCANIA PRESS, Atlantic Ocean, July 19, 1904.

A North Atlantic Communication Chart

(Courtesy Marconi plc)

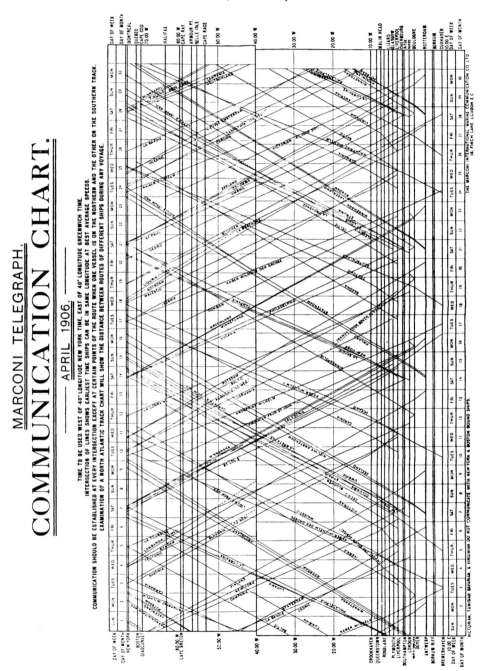

Early Radio-Telegram Charges

(Courtesy Marconi plc)

THE MARCONIGRAPH—Advertisements.

The Transmission of Telegrams to and from Ships at Sea

TELEGRAMS for transmission to ships equipped with Wireless Telegraph apparatus are accepted at nearly every telegraph office in the World. Full information regarding routes, rates, etc., will be found in the British Post Office Official Guide, or may be obtained from any telegraph office or the offices of the Marconi Companies.

Messages may also be transmitted through the Marconi Companies' High Power Stations at Poldhu, England, and Cape Cod, U.S.A., to ships fitted with special receiving apparatus at any point on the North Atlantic, at a charge of 3s. per word.

WIRELESS MESSAGES MAY ALSO BE SENT TO CERTAIN SHIPS THROUGH THE FOLLOWING COAST STATIONS ABROAD—

ADEN.	CHINA.	INDIA.	JAPAN—contd.	RUSSIA.
ALGERIA.	Tsingtau.	Bombay.	Shiomisaki.	Nicolaiewsk.
Fort de l'Eau.	Cocos.	Calcutta.	Tsunoshima.	Petropavlovsk.
AUSTRIA.	CORSICA.	Jask.	MEXICO.	SARDINIA.
Pola.	Ajaccio.	Sandheads.	Cerritos de	Maddalena.
Sebenico.	DENMARK.	ITALY.	Sinaloa	SENEGAL.
AZORES.	Copenhagen.	Asinara.	S. Jose del Cabo.	Dakar.
Corvo.	FRANCE.	Bari.	S. Rosalia de la	Port Etienne.
Fayal.	Boulogne.	Capo Mele.	Baja California.	Rufisque.
Flores.	Brest.	Capo Sperone.	MOROCCO.	SOMALILAND.
S. Maria.	Cherbourg.	Cozzo Spadaro.	Casablanca.	Berbera.
S. Miguel.	Dunkirk.	Forte Spuria.	Mogador.	SOUTH AFRICA.
BELGIUM.	Lorient.	Monte Cappuccini	Rabat.	Cape Town.
Nieuport.	Porquerolles.	Monte San	Tangiers.	Durban.
BRAZIL.	Rochefort.	Giuliano.	NORWAY.	SWEDEN.
Amaralina (Bahia)	S. Maries - de - la	Naples.	Flekkerö.	Karlskrona.
Babylonia (Rio de	Mer.	Palermo.	Röst.	URUGUAY.
Janeiro).	Ushant.	Palmaria.	Sörvaagen.	Cerro de
Fernando	GERMANY.	Ponza.	Tjömö.	Montevideo.
Noronha.	Arkona.	Reggio.		Punta del Este.
Olinda.	Borkum.	S.Maria di Leuca.	PACIFIC ISLANDS.	WEST INDIES.
BRITISH GUIANA.	Bülk.	Venice.	Angaur (Palaos	Curaco.
Demerara.	Cuxhaven.	Viesti.	Islands).	Jamaica.
BURMA.	Norddeich.	JAPAN.	Jap (or Yap)(Caro-	Tobago.
Diamond Island.	HOLLAND.	Choshi.	line Islands).	Trinidad.
Table Island.	Scheveningen	Fukkikaku.		ZANZIBAR.
Victoria Point.	Haven.	Osezaki.	ROUMANIA.	Zanzibar.
		Otchishi.	Constantza.	Pemba.

Passengers on board ships fitted with the Marconi system may obtain from the enquiry office on board, or from the Marconi Operator, full particulars regarding the despatch of messages to all parts of the world.

Any further information required will be willingly supplied on receipt of a request addressed to any one of the following Marconi Offices—

LONDON	. . .	The Marconi International Marine Communication Co., Ltd., Watergate House, York Buildings, Adelphi, W.C.
BRUSSELS	. . .	La Cie de Telegraphie sans Fil, 19 Rue du Champ de Mars.
PARIS	. . . .	La Cie Francaise Maritime et Coloniale de Telegraphie sans Fil, 35 Boulevard des Capucines.
BUENOS AYRES	.	La Cia Marconi de Telegrafia sin Hilos del Rio de la Plata, 132 San Martin.
MADRID	. . .	Cia Nacional de Telegrafia sin Hilos, Calle de Alcala 43.
MONTREAL	.	Marconi Wireless Telegraph Co. of Canada, Ltd., 86 Notre Dame St.
NEW YORK	.	The Marconi Wireless Telegraph Co. of America, 27 William Street.
ROME	. . .	Marquis L. Solari, Piazzi S. Silvestro, 74.

APPENDIX 6

The Prospectus of the Marconi WT Co. Ltd., 1908

(Courtesy Marconi plc and David Evans)

No part of this Issue has been or will be underwritten.

(This Prospectus has been filed with the Registrar of Joint Stock Companies).

The Subscription List will open on Monday, the 1st of June, 1908, and will close on or before Thursday, the 4th of June, 1908, for Town and Country, and Monday, the 8th of June, for the Continent.

MARCONI'S WIRELESS TELEGRAPH COMPANY
LIMITED.

(Incorporated under the Companies Acts, 1862 to 1890).

CAPITAL - - £750,000
DIVIDED INTO

250,000 Seven per cent. Cumulative Participating Preference Shares of £1 each	£250.000
500,000 Ordinary Shares of £1 each (of which 394,190 Shares have been issued and are fully paid)	£500,000
Total Authorised Share Capital	£750,000

The holders of the Preference Shares are entitled to a cumulative preferential dividend of 7 per cent. per annum, on the amount for the time being paid up thereon, and after payment of a dividend of 10 per cent. per annum on the Ordinary Shares, the holders of the Preference Shares have the right each year to participate *pari passu* with the Ordinary Shares in any surplus profits which it shall from time to time be determined to distribute.

The Preference Shares carry equal rights of attending meetings and voting with the Ordinary Shares, and the right in a winding-up to rank in priority to all other shares for the repayment of capital, and *pari passu* with all other shares in any excess after repayment of capital paid up thereon.

PRESENT ISSUE.

The Company now offers for subscription at par 250,000 Seven per cent. Cumulative Participating Preference Shares of £1 each, payable as follows:—

On Application, 2s. 6d. per Share; On Allotment, 2s. 6d. per Share; and the balance in instalments of 5s. per Share, at intervals of not less than Two Months.

The Directors and their friends have applied for 50,000 Shares of the present issue on the terms of this Prospectus.

issue of Cumulative Participating Preference Shares paid in arrear of their respective due dates, and failure to pay any instalment when due will render previous payments liable to forfeiture.

Directors.

COLONEL SIR CHARLES EUAN SMITH, K.C.B., C.S.I. *(Chairman)*, 51, South Street, Mayfair, London, W.
H. JAMESON DAVIS, Killabeg, Enniscorthy, Ireland.
COMMENDATORE G. MARCONI, LL.D., D.Sc. *(Managing Director)*, Watergate House, Adelphi, London, W.C.
ALBERT L. OCHS, 25, Green Street, London, W.
MAJOR S. FLOOD PAGE, 21, Granville Place, London, W.
HENRY S. SAUNDERS, Watergate House, Adelphi, London, W.C.

Bankers.
THE LONDON & COUNTY BANKING COMPANY, LIMITED, 21, Lombard Street, London, E.C.

Solicitors.
HOLLAMS, SONS, COWARD & HAWKSLEY, 30, Mincing Lane, London, E.C.

Brokers.
BILLETT, CAMPBELL & GRENFELL, 3, Throgmorton Avenue, London, E.C.

Auditors.
COOPER BROTHERS & COMPANY, 14, George Street, Mansion House, London, E.C.

Secretary and Registered Offices.
HENRY WILLIAM ALLEN, F.C.I.S., Watergate House, Adelphi, London, W.C.

PROSPECTUS.

THE success achieved by the Marconi system in establishing Wireless Telegraphic Communication between the United Kingdom and Canada, has made it desirable to increase the Capital of the Company so as to enable it to further extend its operations.

The money to be raised by the issue of the Participating Preference Shares now offered for subscription is required, among other purposes, for the further development of the Marconi system, for working capital, and in particular to meet the expenditure and engagements that have been necessary and which have still to be incurred for the final completion of the Transatlantic Stations at Clifden (Co. Galway) and Cape Breton (Canada), by means of which wireless telegraph communication is now carried on between the United Kingdom and America. With the duplication and enlargement of the power plant, and the establishment of landline connections similar to those enjoyed by the cable companies, the Directors are confident that they will be able to provide for the public a speedy and thoroughly efficient direct Wireless Service with America.

It is intended at once to bring up to the same level of efficiency as the Irish-Canadian Stations mentioned the two long-distance stations at Poldhu in England and Cape Cod in the United States of America. When this has been accomplished, there will be two pairs of Marconi high-power stations engaged in the Transatlantic Service, and the Company will then be in a position to accept the many offers of press and other business which it has received, but which it is not at present in a position to undertake.

The Company has an agreement with the British Post Office whereby the latter engages to grant the same facilities for the collection and delivery of messages by the Marconi Transatlantic system, as those offered to the cable companies.

Up to the present the Transatlantic Wireless Telegraph Service has been conducted at speeds varying up to 24 words a minute, but with a comparatively inexpensive modification of certain parts of the existing apparatus, an average speed of at least 30 words a minute should be attained, and further it is expected that it will be possible to send and receive simultaneously at this speed, so that 60 words per minute may be dealt with.

ESTIMATE OF REVENUE FROM TRANSATLANTIC SERVICE ONLY.

On the basis of the improved Irish-Canadian Service, and of the contemplated English-American Service, assuming the four stations are worked for only 12 hours a day, at an average net wireless rate of only 4d. per word, and at a speed of 20 words a minute, a net revenue (after deducting working expenses) approaching £150,000 per annum is capable of being earned. Half of this sum, viz.: £75,000, which would be collected directly by this Company, would be more than sufficient to pay 7 per cent. on the whole of the proposed issue of Preference Shares, and 10 per cent. on the whole of the issued Ordinary Shares.

Estimated net takings of Clifden and Poldhu		£75,000
Dividend, 7 per cent. on £250,000 Cumulative Preference Shares	£17,500	
Dividend, 10 per cent. on £394,190 Ordinary Shares	39,419	
		56,919
Balance available for reserve and further dividends		£18,081

In addition to the total earnings of the two long-distance stations at Poldhu and Clifden, this Company, as the holder of the majority of the issued shares in the American and Canadian Companies, will be entitled to the greater proportion of all dividends declared in respect of the estimated £75,000 profit which would be derived from the corresponding stations at Cape Cod (United States of America) and Cape Breton (Canada).

Reduced facsimiles of a page of the London " Times " and of a page of the " New York Times " showing dispatches transmitted by " Marconi's Trans-Atlantic Wireless Telegraphy," are enclosed with this Prospectus.

ADDITIONAL SOURCES OF REVENUE.

Holdings in Associated Companies.

At the 14th May, 1908, the Company held shares in its affiliated Companies of a par value of £2,453,464. It is not possible at present to make a precise valuation of these assets, but some idea of their value to this Company may be gauged by the fact that these holdings represent more than 50 per cent. of the whole issued capital of these companies, including £200,278 of the £204,056 issued share capital of the Marconi International Marine Communication Company Limited, representing the Marconi wireless exchange of messages at sea.

Maritime

The maritime service is progressing satisfactorily, the North Atlantic being covered by a

increasing. The growth of this service is as follows; warships excluded:—

1905	80 ships
1906	92 ,,
1907	118 ,,

The number of words transmitted and received, calculated from the receipts, was about :—

1905	657,785
1906	1,361,655
1907	1,834,540

The net receipts by the Marconi International Marine Communication Company Limited, and its associated companies from this source for the same period were—

1905	£13,448 0 7
1906	27,858 13 6
1907	37,506 6 4

The same progressive increase both in ships installed, messages transmitted and received, and in revenue, as shown by the above figures, has been fully maintained during the current year. On the establishment of this organisation large sums of money have been spent by the Marconi Wireless Companies, and successful efforts have been made to obtain an equally satisfactory and reliable service on ships of all nations.

The Poldhu station has been supplying a daily press service to such of the Atlantic liners as are fitted with long distance apparatus. The receipts of the Poldhu station from this source alone during the two years ending 29th February, 1908, amounted to over £13,000.

Admiralty Contract.

The Marconi system of Wireless Telegraphy is in use throughout the British Navy and at British naval stations in the United Kingdom and abroad.

Under the terms of a valuable agreement with the Company, the Admiralty continues to utilise the Company's high power stations for communication with the ships of the fleet, whether in home waters, in the Atlantic, or in the Mediterranean, within a radius of 2,000 miles.

Agencies.

The Company has several important Agencies, notably in Italy and Russia. Contracts with the Russian Government of a gross value of £94,599 have been executed. The Italian Government have granted important privileges to Mr. Marconi and this Company for 14 years, under an agreement dated 19th May, 1903. Fifteen Government stations for ship to shore communication are worked by the Italian Government for mercantile purposes, and a high power station is in course of erection at Coltano, Italy, destined for Wireless Telegraphic Communication with Marconi long distance stations in other parts of the world.

Important Contracts.

This Company and its Associated Companies, in which it has the large holdings stated above (amounting in all to over 50 % of the subscribed capital), have important agreements with the British Admiralty, the Post Office, Board of Trade and Trinity House, Italian Government, Newfoundland Government, Canadian Government, Belgian Government and with Lloyd's Corporation. These contracts have resulted in considerable sales of apparatus, and involve payments to the Companies of sums representing a fixed minimum of £13,444 per annum. The special importance of these agreements consists in the assistance they afford in promoting the Company's policy of establishing an organisation for carrying on a public telegraph service by means of wireless telegraph apparatus, both for ship-to-shore communication and for communication between one country and another.

The Company owns over 400 patents, taken out in nearly all the important countries of the world. **Patents.**
When the Company was formed in 1897, communications could only be sent a distance of 10 miles, but as the result of invention and development since that date, communications may now be sent 2,500 miles. The recent patents are of great value, inasmuch as they cover for many years important improvements relating to new transmitters and receivers which secure increased speed and improved syntonization.

The Company owns a fully-equipped factory adequate to cope with the expanding demand for **Manufacture of** instruments and installations. Over 300 wireless stations, exclusive of warships, have already been **Apparatus.** equipped by the Company, and the number is constantly being added to. Considerable orders are received each year from the British Admiralty and foreign governments for wireless telegraph apparatus and accessories. The Marconi system is in use for naval, military or commercial purposes in Canada, Newfoundland, Gibraltar, Malta, Italy, Russia, Belgium, Germany, France, Holland, Montenegro, Chili, Brazil, Argentina, United States of America, Iceland, Siberia, Egypt, Eritrea, China and Siam. This branch of the business may be expected to lead to large and profitable demands for manufactured apparatus.

Mr. G. Marconi has agreed to act as Chief Engineer for not less than three years.

The following information is given in compliance with the provisions of the Companies Act, 1900 :
(1) On the formation of the Company in 1897, 60,000 fully paid up £1 shares were issued as part of the purchase price of the patents and patent rights acquired from Mr. Marconi, of these shares 10,000 fully paid shares were transferred by Mr. Marconi to Mr. Henry Jameson Davis who was a joint promoter with Mr. Marconi of the Company in consideration of the payment by the said Mr. Henry Jameson Davis of the charges and expenses payable in respect of the formation and registration of the Company. In February 1903, 733 fully paid up shares were issued in exchange for 1,833 fully paid shares in The Marconi International Marine Communication Company, Limited. In August 1903, and February 1904, 38,311 fully paid up £1 shares were issued in exchange for shares in the said last-mentioned Company. In July and August 1897, 40,000 £1 shares were offered and issued at par and these shares have been fully paid up. In November 1898, 25,000 shares were offered and in December 1898, 24,583 shares were issued at par and have been fully paid up. In September 1900, 25,000 shares were offered and 12,500 shares were issued at a premium of £2 per share, and have been fully paid up, an underwriting commission of five shillings per share being paid on such 12,500 shares. In August 1901, 40,000 £1 shares were offered at a premium of £1 per share, and in September 1901, 12,736 shares, and in May 1902, 7,264 shares were issued at a premium of £1 per share and have been fully paid up. In May 1904, 25,000 £1 shares were offered and issued at a premium of 5/- per share and have been fully paid up. In October 1904, 30,000 shares were offered and issued at par and have been fully paid up. In March 1906, 128,063 shares were offered and issued at par and have been fully paid up. In November 1905, 5,000 fully paid up shares were issued as part of the purchase price of freehold land and factory premises at Dalston. In May 1908, 10,000 fully paid up £1 shares were allotted to Mr. Henry Cuthbert Hall in consideration of the relinquishment and discharge of the Company from all claims and demands whether for salary, commission or otherwise which were then in dispute.

Apart from the Contracts made by the Company in the ordinary course of business, the following have been entered into within the two years immediately preceding the date hereof :—
13th June, 1906, The Company and Stephen Downey. 12th July, 1906, The Company and The Marconi International Marine Communication Company, Limited, and Guglielmo Cipriani & Co., extended by cable of 3rd December, 1906, and letter from Managing Director of 30th September, 1907. 9th November, 1906, The Company and Alfred Weiss. 9th November, 1906, and 11th November, 1906, The Company and the Buitenlandsche Bankvereeniging. 1st February, 1907, The Company (by G. Marconi) and the Marconi International Marine Communication Company, Limited, and La Cie. de Télégraphie Sans Fil and Il Lloyd Sabaudo. 30th November, 1906, The Company undertaking to pay duties, etc., in France and nomination of representative there. 18th December, 1906, The Company and The Marconi International Marine Communication Company, Limited, and Guglielmo Cipriani & Co. (altered to Jose de Chapeaurouge). 18th December, 1906 (re-executed 24th January, 1907), The Company and The Marconi International Marine Communication Company, Limited, and Alexander Cook and Guglielmo Cipriani & Co. 24th and 25th January, 1907, The Company and Sanfil Limited. 24th January, 1907, The Company and the Marconi International Marine Communication Company, Limited. 26th January, 1907, The Company and E. Kalker & Company. 10th April, 1907, The Company and The Marconi International Marine Communication Company, Limited. 10th April, 1907, The Company and The Marconi International Marine Communication Company, Davis, J. Ferry Goodbody, and T. A. Ferguson. 6th November, 1907, The Company and the London and County Banking Company, Limited. 8th October, 1907, The Company and The Marconi International Marine Communication Company, Limited, and Jose de Chapeaurouge. 28th October, 1907, The Company and Louis Serra di Cassano. 16th and 28th March, 1908, The Company and G. Marconi and The New African Company, Limited. 24th March, 1908, The Company and Gerald F. Talbot. 30th March, 1908, The Company and W. T. Hedges, Limited. 7th, 15th and 16th April, 1908, The Company and G. Marconi and Ochs Brothers. 8th April, 1908, The Company and The Marconi International Marine Communication Company, Limited, and Henry Cuthbert Hall. 16th April, 1908, 15th May, 1908, 16th May, 1908, and 26th May, 1908, The Company and Guglielmo Marconi. 21st May, 1908, The Company and Messrs. Billett, Campbell & Grenfell. On the 24th October, 1907, the Company decided to exercise the right conferred on it by Agreements dated 21st April, 1901, and 10th May, 1902, and made between the Company and Mrs. Emily Mannell Williams, of Angrouse, Mullion, Cornwall, to purchase from the said E. M. Williams, the piece of land on which the Poldhu Station is situated, measuring 9 acres, 3 roods and 11 poles, or thereabouts, at the rate of £200 an acre, which purchase has not yet been completed.

The minimum subscription upon which the Directors will proceed to allotment is 100,000 of the Cumulative Participating Preference Shares now offered for subscription.

Applications should be made on the form accompanying the Prospectus, or appended to the newspaper advertisement, which should be sent together with a cheque for the amount due on application to the London and County Banking Company, Limited, 21, Lombard Street, E.C., or in the case of applications from persons on the Continent, to one of the Banks below-mentioned.

The Directors have also authorised La Banca Commerciale Italiana, at Milan, Genoa, Rome and other Branches ; Credito Italiano, at its Head Office and Branches ; La Compagnie Française Maritime et Coloniale de Télégraphie sans Fil, 35, Boulevard des Capucines, Paris ; and La Compagnie de Télégraphie sans Fil, 19, Rue Brederode, Brussels, to receive applications for the above-mentioned issue.

If no Allotment is made, the deposit will be returned without deduction, and where the number of Shares allotted is less than that applied for, the surplus will be credited in reduction of the amount due on Allotment, and any balance returned without deduction.

The Company will pay the expenses of and incidental to the present issue, including a brokerage of 6d. per Share on each Share allotted on Application Forms bearing Brokers' stamps. The Company will also pay to Foreign Bankers and Agents abroad, through whom approved applications are received, a commission of 1/- per Share in lieu of brokerage.

Copies of the last audited Balance Sheet of the Company, the Memorandum and Articles of Association, and the Contracts hereinbefore mentioned may be inspected at the Registered Offices of the Company in ordinary business hours while the Subscription List remains open.

Copies of the above Contracts and documents may also be similarly inspected at the Offices of the Solicitors to the Company.

Application for a settlement in and a quotation of the Cumulative Participating Preference Shares now offered will be made in due course to the Committee of the London Stock Exchange.

Prospectuses may be obtained at the Head Office of the Company, Watergate House, York Buildings, Adelphi, London, W.C. ; Messrs. Billett, Campbell & Grenfell, 3, Throgmorton Avenue, London, E.C. ; The London & County Banking Company, Limited, 21, Lombard Street, London, E.C. ; La Banca Commerciale Italiana, Milan, Rome and Genoa ; Credito Italiano, Milan and Rome ; La Compagnie Française Maritime et Coloniale de Télégraphie sans Fil, 35, Boulevard des Capucines, Paris ; and La Compagnie de Télégraphie sans Fil, 19, Rue Brederode, Brussels.

Dated 29*th* *May*, 1908.

WATERGATE HOUSE,
    YORK BUILDINGS,
        ADELPHI, LONDON, W.C.

APPENDIX 7

Report of the Directors of the
Marconi Wireless Telegraph Co. Ltd., 1908

(Courtesy Marconi plc and David Evans)

MARCONI'S WIRELESS TELEGRAPH COMPANY,

LIMITED.

REPORT OF THE DIRECTORS

AND

STATEMENT OF ACCOUNTS

For the Period ending 31st December, 1908.

To be presented at the ANNUAL ORDINARY GENERAL MEETING of the Company, at RIVER PLATE HOUSE, FINSBURY CIRCUS, LONDON, E.C., on MONDAY, the 28th June, 1909, at 3 o'clock in the afternoon.

MARCONI'S WIRELESS TELEGRAPH COMPANY, LIMITED.

NOTICE IS HEREBY GIVEN that the TWELFTH ORDINARY GENERAL MEETING of MARCONI'S WIRELESS TELEGRAPH COMPANY, LIMITED, will be held at River Plate House, Finsbury Circus, in the City of London, on Monday, the 28th day of June, 1909, at 3 o'clock in the afternoon, for the purpose of receiving and considering the Statement of Accounts and Balance Sheet, and the Reports of the Directors and Auditors thereon, electing Directors and other officers in the place of those retiring by rotation, and transacting the other ordinary business of the Company.

AND NOTICE IS ALSO HEREBY GIVEN that at the same place and on the same day, at 3.30 o'clock in the afternoon, or so soon thereafter as the business of the Ordinary General Meeting shall be concluded, an EXTRAORDINARY GENERAL MEETING of the above-named Company will be held for the purpose of considering, and, if thought fit, passing the following resolution, that is to say :—

RESOLUTION.

That the Articles of Association of the Company be altered as follows :—

" By substituting the following Article for Article 8, that is to say—

" 8. The Directors may exercise the powers conferred by Section 89 of the Companies (Consolidation) Act, 1908, but so that the commission shall not exceed 30 per cent. on the shares in each case offered. As regards all allotments of the Company's shares from time to time made, the Directors shall comply with Section 88 of the Companies (Consolidation) Act, 1908."

Should the above resolution be passed by the requisite majority, it will be submitted for confirmation as a special resolution at a further Extraordinary General Meeting of the Company which will be subsequently convened.

The Transfer Books of the Company will be closed from the 26th day of June to the 10th day of July, 1909, both days inclusive.

By order of the Board,
HENRY W. ALLEN,
Secretary.

WATERGATE HOUSE, ADELPHI,
LONDON, W.C.
18*th June*, 1909.

NOTE.—If this notice comes into the hands of any holder of a share warrant of the above Company who wishes to attend the said meetings, such holder is reminded that share warrants must be deposited at the office of the Company at least three days before the date of the meetings.

MARCONI'S WIRELESS TELEGRAPH COMPANY, LIMITED.

CAPITAL   -   -   -   £750,000,

DIVIDED INTO

250,000 Seven per cent. Cumulative Participating Preference Shares of £1 each, and

500,000 Ordinary Shares of £1 each.

Directors.

COMMENDATORE G. MARCONI, LL.D., D.Sc. *(Chairman and Managing Director)*.

H. JAMESON DAVIS.

COLONEL SIR CHARLES EUAN-SMITH, K.C.B., C.S.I.

SAMUEL GEOGHEGAN, M.I.M.E., M.I.C.E.I.

MAJOR S. FLOOD PAGE.

HENRY S. SAUNDERS.

Auditors.

COOPER BROTHERS & CO.

Solicitors.

HOLLAMS, SONS, COWARD & HAWKSLEY.

Brokers.

BILLETT, CAMPBELL & GRENFELL, 3, Throgmorton Avenue, London, E.C.

Secretary and Offices.

HENRY W. ALLEN, F.C.I.S., Watergate House, Adelphi, London, W.C.

REPORT OF DIRECTORS.

The Directors have the honour to present to the Shareholders the following Report of the Company's affairs with Balance Sheet up to the 31st December, 1908.

The Shareholders will remember that at the last General Meeting of the Company sanction was given to the increase of the capital of the Company by the creation of 250,000 seven per cent. Preference Shares of £1 each. The public issue was duly made and 125,080 Preference Shares were subscribed for. Although this amount was short of the sum necessary to carry out the entire programme outlined in the Prospectus, it was nevertheless sufficient to meet the Company's current engagements, and to provide for the expenditure required to complete the transatlantic stations at Clifden and Glace Bay, and in addition allowed the carrying out of a scheme of re-organisation of the works. The works have now been placed on a thoroughly profitable working basis.

The close attention of the Directors has been given to the completion of the transatlantic stations at Clifden (Ireland) and Glace Bay (Canada), which has occupied a large portion of Mr. Marconi's time, and although there have been serious delays in the delivery of important sections of the electrical plant, it is now a matter of great satisfaction to the Directors to be able to state that the Clifden Station is actually complete and fully able to carry out the transmission and reception of transatlantic messages to the extent stated in the Prospectus issued on the 29th May, 1908.

The machinery required for the completion and duplication of the station at Glace Bay is also ready, and nearly all delivered and erected, but it will be necessary for Mr. Marconi to visit Glace Bay before the Company can undertake the extension of the transatlantic service, which may be anticipated so soon as the Post Office gives effect to the agreement relative to the acceptance and delivery of Marconi transatlantic messages at all the Government Telegraph Offices throughout the United Kingdom, which will be probably about the end of August.

It will be observed that the accounts cover a period of 15 months. The Directors thought it advisable to make the Company's Annual Report and Accounts synchronize with the calendar year—hence the delay in publishing this report.

The Directors regret that at present they are not able to declare the payment of a dividend. They feel, notwithstanding this, that the prospects and position of the Company are now highly satisfactory and promising, and they confidently anticipate that the dividend-paying period will speedily be entered upon. The remunerative business is extending in every direction. Economies have been effected wherever such have been found possible. Expenses have been cut down in all directions and the field of profitable operation is steadily and persistently extending throughout the world. The Directors feel that the difficulties always attending the development of so great and novel an enterprise as this are at last yielding to the results of knowledge and experience, and profitable returns are now well within sight.

With these preliminary remarks the report will proceed to deal with the progress of the Company in the various parts of the world.

7

INTERNATIONAL COMPANY.

The Directors are glad to be able to say that the fears which they at one time entertained that the ratification of the Berlin Convention by His Majesty's Government would be detrimental to the maritime business of the Associated Marconi Companies have so far not been realised, and indeed a considerable addition has been made to the number of ships fitted and working the Marconi system, a list of which will be found in the appendix.

The maritime business of the International Company continues to expand in a most satisfactory manner. Marconi apparatus is already installed on 185 mercantile ships for the purpose of a public telegraph service, and 38 ships are being equipped, including vessels of the Peninsular and Oriental Steam Navigation Company, Royal Mail Steam Packet Company, Koninklijke Hollandsche Lloyd, L'Unione Austriaca di Navigazione, Societa di Navigazione a Vapore Italia and the Wilson Line.

CANADA.

Our relations with the Canadian Government continue to be most satisfactory, and orders for the equipment of new Marconi stations at Montreal and Three Rivers are in course of execution by the Canadian Company.

Mr. Marconi and Mr. H. Jameson Davis visited Canada last autumn for the purpose of conferring with the Directors of that Company, with the result that improvements leading to considerable economies have been effected in the organisation.

The duplication and enlargement of the transatlantic station at Glace Bay is almost complete, and, as stated above, it is expected that by means of this station and that at Clifden in Ireland, a speedy and thoroughly efficient direct wireless service between Europe and America will be provided in the month of August.

UNITED STATES.

The long distance station at Cape Cod, which is at present employed in supplying a daily news service to ships fitted with Marconi long distance receiving apparatus will, as soon as possible, be brought up to the same degree of efficiency as at the station at Clifden. With the completion of this station and the transatlantic station at Poldhu, Cornwall, there will be two pairs of high power stations available for the transatlantic service. Negotiations are now proceeding for the establishment in New York City of a station to receive and distribute messages from Glace Bay and Cape Cod.

ARGENTINA AND URUGUAY.

Mr. Marconi will visit Buenos Ayres in the autumn to arrange for the erection of a high power station in the Argentine Republic, primarily to communicate with the high power station in course of erection at Coltano in Italy.

8

The operations of the Argentine Marconi Company are being steadily extended. Apparatus has been purchased by the Argentine Government for navy purposes and Marconi stations have been opened at Bernal and San Martin and at Punta del Este in the Republic of Uruguay.

FRANCE.

The Compagnie Française Maritime et Coloniale de Telegraphie sans Fil is making satisfactory progress and an arrangement is in prospect with the French Government for the erection of long distance stations and for other developments of the greatest importance to France and her colonies, and to this Company.

BRAZIL.

This Company has secured the contract, on satisfactory terms, for the equipment with the Marconi system of ten torpedo boat destroyers, two battleships, and two scouts, which are being built in this country to the order of the Brazilian Government. The work is now proceeding, four of the destroyers having already been completed and payment received in respect of them.

The Company has also secured the contract from the Hydrographical Department of Brazil for the equipment of the lighthouses at Ilha Raza, Ponta Negra and Guaratiba, and for the erection of a station at Rio de Janeiro to communicate with them. The apparatus for these stations has been delivered in Brazil, and the work of erection is proceeding and is expected to be completed very shortly. Part payment has already been received under this contract.

MADEIRA-MAMORE RAILWAY COMPANY.

The Brazilian Madeira-Mamore Railway is intended to connect Porto Velho at the head of the navigable waters of the Madeira River with Guajara-Mirim, above which it is reckoned that there are some 4,000 miles of navigable rivers flowing through countries rich in the best quality of india rubber. Neither of these places being in telegraphic communication with the outside world, the Madeira-Mamore Railway obtained a concession for the erection and operation of wireless stations at Porto Velho and Manaos, the latter place being a cable station on the Amazon Telegraph Company's system. The Board is happy to inform you that the contract for these stations has been awarded to the Company, the price for the work, which it is expected will be completed in December next, being £35,800.

BELGIUM.

The Compagnie de Telegraphie sans Fil of Brussels has considerably increased the number of ships carrying the Marconi system, and continues to conduct a remunerative business.

BULGARIA.

The Bulgarian Government has awarded to the Company the contract for the supply and erection of a station at Varna with a 300-mile working range for ship-to-shore communication.

9

ITALY.

The whole of the Italian Navy has been fitted with the Marconi apparatus and the system is also in daily use on 37 ships of the Italian Mercantile Marine; 18 land stations are likewise available for communication with ships fitted with Marconi apparatus.

The completion of the long distance station at Coltano was for some time delayed, as it was felt desirable to take advantage of the experience gained in the completion of the Irish-Canadian stations, but the work has now been resumed, and the station should this year be available for communication with England and America.

The Directors take this opportunity of again expressing their sense of obligation to the Government of Italy for the assistance which it has given, and continues to give, to the expansion of the Marconi system.

A long distance Marconi station is in course of erection in the Italian Somaliland, which will presently form an important link between Europe and the Far East.

PATENTS.

Over 600 patents are now owned by the Marconi Companies. Several of the patents recently taken out cover important improvements, thus further improving the patent position of the Company.

MANUFACTURE OF APPARATUS.

The Directors after careful consideration determined that it was desirable to close their Dalston factory and return to their former factory at Chelmsford. The necessary machinery and stores were accordingly transferred to Chelmsford in August last, and the Dalston factory leased on satisfactory terms to Messrs. Siemens Brothers & Company, Limited. Since the removal to Chelmsford the works have been fully occupied with the execution of orders from the British Admiralty, foreign governments and the associated companies for wireless telegraph apparatus and accessories. The value of the orders in hand at this date amounts to over £87,000.

The Directors cannot close this report without again calling attention to the utility of wireless telegraphy in the case of ships in distress, which has never been more strikingly demonstrated than in the accident which resulted in the loss of the White Star Liner, " Republic," on January 23rd last.

The service rendered by the Marconi system on this occasion has been commented upon extensively, but the Directors venture to refer to this unfortunate accident as illustrating the excellent working of the Marconi ship-to-ship and ship-to-shore telegraph organisation. As the

10

result of the collision with the " Florida," the wireless cabin was very badly wrecked and the apparatus itself somewhat damaged. However, the operator, Mr. J. R. Binns, with considerable promptitude and resource speedily effected the necessary repairs and immediately established communication with the Marconi shore station at Siasconset on Nantucket Island. This station thereupon signalled the " Baltic," the " La Lorraine " and numerous other vessels equipped with our apparatus to such good effect that no less than seven vessels fitted with the Marconi system were forthwith ready to lend aid, with the happy result which is well known. While the operators deserve thanks for their untiring service, the Directors think that the good discipline maintained and the efficiency of the installation on board the fitted vessels afford satisfactory proof of the great value of the Marconi organisation to not only the Shareholders, but also to all transatlantic travellers.

Still more recently, indeed since this report was put into type, the wreck of the " Slavonia " has afforded another opportunity for demonstrating the gratifying extent to which the Marconi system may be utilised in the saving of human life. Full details are not yet to hand, but from information received it would appear that at about 2.30 o'clock on Thursday morning, the 10th June, 1909, the " Slavonia " stranded on Flores Island in the Azores. Fortunately the ship was fitted with Marconi wireless apparatus, and consequently was able to effect communication with the " Batavia," also carrying Marconi apparatus, at a distance of 150 miles, and afterwards with the " Prinzessin Irene," similarly fitted. Both ships on being called immediately went to the assistance of the wrecked vessel. All the " Slavonia's " passengers, numbering 410, were successfully transferred to these two ships and were brought safely to port without the loss of a single life.

The disaster to the " Slavonia," coming so soon after the accident to the " Republic," and the enormous value of wireless on these ships having been in both cases thoroughly demonstrated, it is to be hoped that all maritime nations will enact laws rendering the installation of wireless telegraphy compulsory on all sea-going passenger vessels.

In December, 1908, Mr. Samuel Geoghegan of The Grove, Killiney, County Dublin, was elected to a seat on the Board, and in January last Mr. Albert L. Ochs resigned his directorship.

The Directors retiring by rotation are Colonel Sir Charles Euan-Smith, K.C.B., C.S.I., and Mr. Henry Jameson Davis, who being eligible, offer themselves for re-election.

The Auditors, Messrs. Cooper Brothers & Co., also retire and offer themselves for re-appointment.

By order of the Board,

HENRY W. ALLEN,

Secretary.

WATERGATE HOUSE,
    YORK BUILDINGS,
        ADELPHI, LONDON, W.C.
    15th June, 1909.

11

MARCONI WIRELESS EXCHANGE.

Particulars of Vessels fitted with the Marconi System of Wireless Telegraphy.

LINE.	VESSEL.
ABERDEEN LINE	Inanda
,, ,,	Inkosi
ALLAN LINE	Corsican
,, ,,	Grampian
,, ,,	Hesperian
,, ,,	Tunisian
,, ,,	Victorian
,, ,,	Virginian
AMERICAN LINE	New York
,, ,,	Philadelphia
,, ,,	St. Louis
,, ,,	St. Paul
ANCHOR LINE	Caledonia
,, ,,	California
,, ,,	Columbia
,, ,,	Furnessia
ANGLO-AMERICAN OIL COMPANY, LIMITED	Iroquois
,, ,, ,,	Narragansett
,, ,, ,,	Navahoe
,, ,, ,,	Tamarac
ATLANTIC TRANSPORT LINE	Minneapolis
,, ,,	Minnehaha
,, ,,	Minnetonka
,, ,,	Minnewaska
AUSTRIAN LLOYD S.S. COMPANY, LIMITED	Thalia
BATAVIER LINE	Batavier II.
,, ,,	Batavier III.
,, ,,	Batavier IV.
,, ,,	Batavier V.
BELGIAN ROYAL MAIL	La Flandre
,, ,,	La Rapide
,, ,,	Leopold II.
,, ,,	Marie Henriette
,, ,,	Prince Albert
,, ,,	Princesse Clementine
,, ,,	Princesse Elizabeth

12

LINE.	VESSEL.
BELGIAN ROYAL MAIL	Princesse Henriette
" "	Princesse Josephine
" "	Ville de Douvres
BOOTH LINE...	Antony
CANADIAN GOVERNMENT	Canada
" "	Lady Laurier
" "	Minto
" "	Montcalm
" "	Stanley
CANADIAN PACIFIC RAILWAY COMPANY	Empress of Britain
" " "	Empress of China
" " "	Empress of India
" " "	Empress of Ireland
" " "	Empress of Japan
" " "	Lake Champlain
" " "	Lake Erie
" " "	Lake Manitoba
" " "	Lake Michigan
" " "	Milwaukee
" " "	Monmouth
" " "	Montcalm
" " "	Montezuma
" " "	Montfort
" " "	Montreal
" " "	Montrose
" " "	Mount Royal
" " "	Mount Temple
COMMERCIAL CABLE COMPANY	Mackay Bennett
CIE GENERALE TRANSATLANTIQUE	La Chicago
" "	La Bretagne
" "	La Gascogne
" "	La Lorraine
" "	La Provence
" "	La Savoie
" "	La Touraine
CUNARD LINE	Campania
" "	Carmania
" "	Caronia
" "	Carpathia
" "	Etruria

13

LINE.	VESSEL.
CUNARD LINE	Ivernia
,, ,,	Lucania
,, ,,	Lusitania
,, ,,	Mauretania
,, ,,	Pannonia
,, ,,	Saxonia
,, ,,	Slavonia
,, ,,	Ultonia
,, ,,	Umbria
DOMINION LINE	Canada
,, ,,	Dominion
HAMBURG AMERIKA LINE	Amerika
,, ,,	Batavia
,, ,,	Bluecher
,, ,,	Bulgaria
,, ,,	Cincinnati
,, ,,	Cleveland
,, ,,	Deutschland
,, ,,	Graf Waldersee
,, ,,	Hamburg
,, ,,	Kaiserin Augusta Victoria
,, ,,	Moltke
,, ,,	Patricia
,, ,,	Pennsylvania
,, ,,	President Grant
,, ,,	President Lincoln
,, ,,	Pretoria
,, ,,	Prinz Adalbert
,, ,,	Prinz Oskar
HOLLAND AMERIKA LIJN	Nieuw Amsterdam
,, ,,	Noordam
,, ,,	Potsdam
,, ,,	Rotterdam
,, ,,	Ryndam
,, ,,	Statendam
KONINKLIJKE HOLLANDSCHE LLOYD	Hollandia
L'UNIONE AUSTRIACA DI NAVIGAZIONE	Alice
,, ,, ,,	Argentina
,, ,, ,,	Laura
,, ,, ,,	Martha Washington
,, ,, ,,	Oceania

14

LINE.	VESSEL.
LA VELOCE NAVIGAZIONE ITALIANA	Europa
,, ,, ,, ...	Nord Amerika
,, ,, ,, ...	Amerika
LLOYD ITALIANO	Principessa Mafalda
,, ,, ...	Virginia
LLOYD SABAUDO	Principe di Piemonte
,, ,, ...	Re d'Italia
,, ,, ...	Regina d'Italia
,, ,, ...	Tomaso di Savoia
NAVIGAZIONE GENERALE ITALIANA	Duca degli Abruzzi
,, ,, ,, ...	Duca di Genova
,, ,, ,, ...	Liguria
,, ,, ,, ...	Lombardia
,, ,, ,, ...	Re Vittorio
,, ,, ,, ...	Sardegna
,, ,, ,, ...	Sicilia
,, ,, ,, ...	Umbria
NEW YORK, NEWFOUNDLAND AND HALIFAX STEAMSHIP COMPANY, LIMITED	Florizel
NORDDEUTSCHER LLOYD	Berlin
,, ,, ...	Friedrich de Grosse
,, ,, ...	George Washington
,, ,, ...	Grosser Kurfurst
,, ,, ...	Kaiser Wilhelm der Grosse
,, ,, ...	Kaiser Wilhelm II.
,, ,, ...	Koenig Albert
,, ,, ...	Koenigin Luise
,, ,, ...	Kronprinz Wilhelm
,, ,, ...	Kronprinzessin Cecilie
,, ,, ...	Main
,, ,, ...	Neckar
,, ,, ...	Prinzessin Alice
,, ,, ...	Prinzessin Irene
,, ,, ...	Prinz Friedrich Wilhelm
,, ,, ...	Rhein
PENINSULAR AND ORIENTAL STEAM NAVIGATION COMPANY	Malwa
,, ,, ,, ,,	Mantua
RED STAR LINE	Finland
,, ,, ...	Kroonland

15

LINE.	VESSEL.
RED STAR LINE	Lapland
,, ,,	Vaderland
,, ,,	Zeeland
REID NEWFOUNDLAND COMPANY	Bruce
ROYAL MAIL STEAM PACKET COMPANY	Avon
SOCIETA DI NAVIGAZIONE A VAPORE ITALIA	Ancona
,, ,, ,,	Taormina
,, ,, ,,	Verona
TRINITY HOUSE LIGHT SHIPS	Cross-sand
,, ,,	Sunk
,, ,,	Tongue
,, ,,	Gull
,, ,,	E. Goodwin
,, ,,	S. Goodwin
WHITE STAR LINE	Adriatic
,, ,,	Arabic
,, ,,	Baltic
,, ,,	Canopic
,, ,,	Cedric
,, ,,	Celtic
,, ,,	Cretic
,, ,,	Cymric
,, ,,	Laurentic
,, ,,	Majestic
,, ,,	Megantic
,, ,,	Oceanic
,, ,,	Romanic
,, ,,	Teutonic
WILSON LINE	Aaro
,, ,,	Oslo

In addition, the following ships are being fitted with Marconi apparatus:—

COMPAGNIE CYPRIEN FABRE	Germania
,, ,,	Madonna
,, ,,	Roma
,, ,,	Venezia
ISLE OF MAN STEAM PACKET COMPANY	Ben my Chree
,, ,,	Empress Queen
,, ,,	Viking
KONINKLIJKE HOLLANDSCHE LLOYD	Frisia

16

LINE.	VESSEL.
L'UNIONE AUSTRIACA DI NAVIGAZIONE	Francesca
" "	Oceania
" "	Sofia Hohenberg
LA VELOCE NAVIGAZIONE ITALIANA	Argentina
" "	Brasile
LLOYD ITALIANO	Cordova
" "	Indiana
" "	Luisiania
" "	Mendoza
" "	Florida
NAVIGAZIONE GENERALE ITALIANA	Campania
" " "	Lazio
" " "	Principe Umberto
" " "	Regina Elena
" " "	Sannio
NEW YORK, NEWFOUNDLAND AND HALIFAX STEAMSHIP COMPANY, LIMITED	Rosalind
NORDDEUTSCHER LLOYD	Barbarossa
PENINSULAR AND ORIENTAL STEAM NAVIGATION COMPANY	Morea
ROYAL MAIL STEAM PACKET COMPANY	Amazon
" " "	Aragon
" " "	Araguaya
" " "	Asturias
SICULA AMERICANA	San Giorgio
" "	San Giovanni
SOCIETA DI NAVIGAZIONE A VAPORE ITALIA	Bologna
" " "	Siena
" " "	Toscana
TELEGRAPH MAINTENANCE AND CONSTRUCTION COMPANY, LIMITED	Colonia
WHITE STAR LINE	Olympic
" "	Titanic

ACCOUNTS.

MARCONI'S WIRELESS TELEGRAPH COMPANY, LIMITED.

BALANCE SHEET.

Dr. | **31st December, 1908.** | **Cr.**

	£ s. d.	£ s. d.	£ s. d.
To CAPITAL:—			
Authorised.			
500,000 Ordinary Shares of £1 each ...	500,000 0 0		
250,000 7 per cent. Cumulative Participating Preference Shares of £1 each ...	250,000 0 0		
	£750,000 0 0		
Issued:			
394,190 Ordinary Shares of £1 each, fully paid ...		394,190 0 0	
125,080 7 per cent. Cumulative Participating Preference Shares of £1 each—			
124,908 Shares with 15s. called up thereon ...	93,681 0 0		
172 „ 10s. „ „ ...	86 0 0		
	93,767 0 0		
Add Amounts paid in advance	16,150 0 0		
	109,917 0 0		
Less Calls in arrear	1,463 17 6	108,453 2 6	502,643 2 6
To SHARE PREMIUM ACCOUNT after charging Expenses of Preference Share issue			13,938 12 1
To RESERVE, being amount of Valuation of Freehold Works at Dalston, in excess of cost, see per contra			22,967 12 0
To CREDITORS:—			
LOANS FROM BANKERS AGAINST SECURITY per contra AND LIEN ON ADMIRALTY ROYALTY	51,908 6 8		
SUNDRY CREDITORS FOR TRADE DEBTS	8,940 0 4		
RESERVE FOR EXPENSES UNPAID, ROYALTY IN ADVANCE AND OTHER AMOUNTS	9,981 10 10		
BILLS PAYABLE	3,624 6 0	74,449 3	
To LIABILITIES ON BILLS DISCOUNTED AND FOR AMOUNTS UNCALLED ON SHARES IN ASSOCIATED COMPANIES	£68,302 16 0		
		£613,998 10	

	£ s. d.	£ s. d.	£ s. d.
By CASH AT BANKERS and in hand			1,777 3 6
By DEBTORS—			11,366 3 11
By AMOUNTS DUE FROM ASSOCIATED COMPANIES, including £122,561. 5s. 1d. due by Canadian Company			142,016 6 11
By STOCK AT COST OR UNDER as certified by the Works Manager			23,683 14 8
By FREEHOLD WORKS AT DALSTON—As per Valuation by Messrs. Fuller, Horsey, Sons & Cassell, as a going concern, dated 3rd March, 1908	61,585 0 0		
Deduct Mortgage	20,111 12 4		
	41,473 7 8		
See Reserve per contra	1,380 19 8	42,854 7 4	
By PLANT AND MACHINERY AT DALSTON WORKS, including £604 Additions ...			
By PLANT AND MACHINERY AT CHELMSFORD WORKS			3,417 17 3
By LONG DISTANCE FREEHOLD STATIONS:—CLIFDEN, IRELAND, AND POLDHU, CORNWALL, INCLUDING PLANT, MACHINERY AND STORES	89,287 11 5		
Deduct Mortgage on land at Poldhu ...	965 15 0	88,321 16 5	
By OTHER STATIONS, INCLUDING PLANT, MACHINERY AND STORES ...			2,612 7 10
By MOVABLE PLANT AT CHELMSFORD AND OTHER PLACES			4,790 4 3
By OFFICE FURNITURE AND FITTINGS AT HEAD OFFICE, CHELMSFORD WORKS AND ROME ...			2,085 12 5
By PATENTS AND SHARES AND DEBENTURES IN ASSOCIATED COMPANIES—			
200,278 fully-paid Shares of £1 each of The Marconi International Marine Communication Company, Limited	200,278 0 0		
80 Seven per cent. First Mortgage Debentures of £500 each of The Marconi International Marine Communication Company, Limited ...	40,000 0 0		
883,021 fully-paid Shares of $5 each Series "A" of Cia Marconi de Telegrafia sin hilos del Rio de la Plata (Argentine Company) ...	883,021 0 0		
88,250 Shares of $5 each (25 per cent. paid) Series "B" of Cia Marconi de Telegrafia sin hilos del Rio de la Plata (Argentine Company)	22,069 10 0		
34,224 fully-paid Shares of $100 each of The Marconi Wireless Telegraph Company of America	684,480 0 0		
614,855 fully-paid Shares of $5 each of The Marconi Wireless Telegraph Company of Canada, Limited	614,855 0 0		
273 Bearer Shares of 1,000 Florins each of Maatschappij voor Radiotelegraphie	22,750 0 0		
60 Bearer Shares (Parts Beneficiaires) of no capital denomination of Cie Francaise Maritime et Coloniale de Telegraphie sans Fil ...	... ...	291,092 16 0	
Total Par Value	£2,415,446 10 0		
			£613,998 10 6

G. MARCONI, *Director.*
S. FLOOD PAGE, *Director.*

Report of the Auditors to the Shareholders.

We have audited the above Balance Sheet. The item, Patents and Shares and Debentures in Associated Companies, referred to in our last report has been increased by the addition of the excess of expenditure over income. This item includes shares of the par value of £1,928,997. 10s. which are in Montreal, New York and Buenos Ayres. We have seen a letter from a Trust Company and from Solicitors stating that the certificates of the shares respectively in Montreal and New York are held on behalf of the Company, subject to a charge in favour of the London and County Banking Company, Limited, and for the shares held at Buenos Ayres we have seen a letter from the Manager of the Argentine Company stating that 660 "A" shares are in the Company's possession.

646,840 "A" Shares are deposited for safe custody with the Banco de Italia y Rio de la Plata, and 88,250 "B" Shares are held by the London and Brazilian Bank, Limited. Evidence of title for only 18 shares in the Maatschappij voor Radiotelegraphie has been produced to us. We have obtained all the information and explanations we have required. In our opinion such Balance Sheet is properly drawn up so as to exhibit a true and correct view of the state of the Company's affairs according to the best of our information and the explanations given us and as shown by the books of the Company.

COOPER BROTHERS & CO. } *Auditors.*
Chartered Accountants, }

London, 15th June, 1909.

A Rival Bid

(Courtesy David Evans)

This Prospectus has been filed with the Registrar of Joint Stock Companies.

The Subscription List will open on Friday, the 6th day of August, 1909, and will close on or before Wednesday, the 11th day of August, 1909.

THE JOHNSON SECRET WIRELESS TELEGRAPH

AND

TELEPHONE TESTING SYNDICATE LIMITED.

(Incorporated under the Companies' Acts, 1862 to 1900.)

AUTHORISED CAPITAL - £15,000,

IN SHARES OF £1 EACH.

Of which 12,521 have been already allotted and are fully paid.

Issue of REMAINING 2,479 Shares of £1 each at par, payable as follows :—

5 - per Share on Application ; 5 - per Share on Allotment ; 10 - per Share Two Months after Allotment.

The Shares now offered will rank *pari passu* with the existing Shares.

Directors.

FRANCIS GRAHAM LLOYD, 40, King Street, E.C., *Chairman*
ARTHUR THOMAS METCALF JOHNSON, A.M.M.C.I.E., 77, Shepherds Bush Road, W.., *Joint*
WILLIAM FREDERICK CHARLES MICHAELIS, 66, Basinghall Street, E.C., *Managing Directors.*
EDWIN JOSEPH RICHARDSON, 41, Brook Street, W.
WILH. HOHNER, Trossingen, Wuerttemberg, Germany.

Bankers.

THE LONDON CITY & MIDLAND BANK, LIMITED, 129, New Bond Street, London, W.

Solicitors.

LAWSON LEWIS, WELCH & WENHAM, 11, John Street, Bedford Row, London, W.C.

Auditors.

JAMES ALEXANDER ROBERTSON & CO., Chartered Accountants, 38 & 39, Billiter Square Buildings, Billiter Street, E.C.

Technical Adviser.

FREDERICK HENRY VARLEY, M.I.E.E., F.R.A.S., 82, Newington Green Road, Islington, N.

Secretary and Registered Offices.

R. G. FUDGE, 40, King Street, Cheapside, London, E.C.

PROSPECTUS.

This Syndicate was incorporated for the purpose of testing and developing a secret tuning system for wireless telegraphy, so as to prevent the tapping of messages, and the delay or loss of messages owing to the interference of one station or ship with another.

An experimental station was equipped at Norman's Bay, near Eastbourne, under license from the Postmaster-General, with suitable plant for producing the necessary electrical power, and a mast 145½ feet high was erected.

The Syndicate secured the services of Mr. A. T. M. Johnson, A.M.M.C.I.E., and satisfactory progress was made, with the gratifying result that absolute secrecy and differentiation of messages by "wireless" were secured with apparatus suitable for short distances.

The Syndicate called in the able Consulting Expert, Mr. Fredk. Satchwell, M.I.E.E., to report upon the results achieved. Extracts from his reports are given below :—

"WIMBLEDON, 12*th March*, 1907.

Messrs. THE JOHNSON SECRET WIRELESS TELEGRAPH AND TELEPHONE TESTING SYNDICATE LTD.
GENTLEMEN,

. . . . . My inspection of all the instruments and observation of demonstrations therefore enables me to state that I found them all carried out according to the principles of the claims in the Specifications mentioned in the former part of this Report, and adhering to the general arrangements therein described and with no other instruments or apparatus other than those so described, the whole being highly satisfactory and in full accord with the claims made.

(Signed) FRED. SATCHWELL, M.I.E.E.
(*Late Superintendent and Manager for Sir Hiram S. Maxim, and The Hiram S. Maxim Electrical Corporation*)."

"JESMOND DENE, PRINCES ROAD, WIMBLEDON,
GENTLEMEN, 25*th March*, 1907.

JOHNSON SECRET WIRELESS TELEGRAPH SYSTEM.

In reference to the two points raised by your letter of 16th inst., namely, **long distance messages and commercial utility**, my reply is that granted the production of electrical waves of any amplitude, and the power to energise the waves, of which there is no doubt, as evidenced by every system of wireless telegraphy, then **the Johnson system can both transmit and receive such messages, either long or short distances**. The question of distance is somewhat governed by the energy produced, but also by pitch, just as a shrill whistle is heard (up to a point in the human ear but to almost any degree in some insects) further than a deeper one, **so a highly-tuned message can be transmitted further than one not so governed** ; the Johnson System **has governing media for telling or denoting such messages** (absent in other systems) and delivering the same. These are dealt with in my previous Report. I am, therefore, of the opinion that the Johnson System will, with full equipped Stations, **transmit and receive any desired secret message, any distance**, that any form of wireless telegraphy can be sent. **The special feature of this system is that it can tune and govern the messages**. Whatever amplitude of vibrations are produced, the Johnson System can speak them and receive them by means of the apparatus described in the previous Report dealing with the Specifications.

As to the commercial utility, this is answered practically by the former being accomplished. Send and receive **secret messages at will, and the commercial side is evident**. There are, however, **special commercial advantages over other systems**, i.e., simplicity of apparatus ; operators are less liable to danger from shocks by use of an adjunct instrument used with the speaking instrument ; the special form of duplicate relays used in the receiving stations (which can be multiplied to any required number) enabling messages to be sent to any number of ships manœuvring at sea, each ship receiving from the transmitting station (either flag ship or on land) a distinct and separate message to that of any other, whilst no ship can receive any message other than that intended for it. So with offices and newspapers or any form of administrative departments. The question of commercial utility in this, as in that of other inventions, also depends on the persons engaged in managing the organisation under which such are to work and develop. This is not without importance. **You will gather from the above that my opinion on the two points in question is distinctly favourable.**

(Signed) FRED. SATCHWELL, M.I.E.E.
The Directors,
THE JOHNSON SECRET WIRELESS TELEGRAPH AND TELEPHONE TESTING SYNDICATE LTD."

To develop and improve Mr. Johnson's invention by making the same applicable for long distance messages, the Directors secured the services of Mr. Fredk. H. Varley, M.I.E.E., F.R.A.S., an expert in wireless telegraphy, who applied himself to produce apparatus which would enable the above System to be adapted to the high power currents used in long distance wireless telegraphy. This is believed to have now been fully accomplished, and Mr. Varley's invention has been patented, and the Syndicate has agreed to acquire his rights to the same under two Agreements, the one made between Mr. Varley and Dr. Richardson, and dated the 12th day of December, 1907, and the other between Mr. Varley and the Johnson Syndicate, and dated the 21st day of June, 1909, copies of which can be seen at the Company's Office at any time.

This secret and differentiating system is intended to be utilized with other existing systems of wireless telegraphy, rendering such systems immune from accidental or intentional interference, drowning of messages, or "tapping" ; and the revenue to be derived from this source only, apart from others, should be of immense profit to the Syndicate. The main thing necessary to make wireless telegraphy as hitherto used a commercial success, is the long needed tuning of the messages. The following recent extracts from the Press, of which many could be given, will serve to show the inconvenience, danger and delay in existing wireless telegraphy :—

From "THE GEWERBEBLATT AUS WURTTEMBURG," May 27th. 1905.

(*Translation.*)

" . . . . There exist eight public coast stations for wireless telegraphy, each of which is able to send messages within an area of 200 kilometres radius. Within this circle the conduct of wireless communications has been transferred to them. It must not be forgotten that the signals given by a station or a ship are noticed by all wireless receiving stations within the same circle. If several stations within a certain radius would send messages simultaneously a confusion would arise, exactly in the same way as if several persons commenced speaking simultaneously in one and the same room. The public station is therefore entitled to give a 'silence' signal, after which all apparatus receiving such must be silent ; the station then calls upon one after the other to speak."

"NEW YORK TIMES." March 15th, 1909.
"Amateur Wireless Interference.

To the Editor of the 'New York Times.'

In the case of the collision between the 'Horatio Hall' and the 'H. F. Dimock,' the operator on the 'Hall' tried to give the location of the disaster, but the interference of a number of amateur operators in the zone of trouble simply made it impossible for him to get word to the revenue cutters or the shore stations. the messages becoming a jumble of sounds with no meaning whatever.

If this practice is longer permitted by the Government officials, it will be useless for steamships to have the wireless equipment. (Signed) FLETCHER DU BOIS. New York, *March* 12th, 1909."

"DAILY TELEGRAPH," June 14th. 1909.

" . . . . The 'Slavonia' struck on the rocks two miles to the south of Flores Island, during a dense fog, and after **twelve hours' work by wireless**, the 'Slavonia', located the North German Lloyd steamer 'Princess Irene' 180 miles to the westward, and **an hour later** picked up the Hamburg-Amerika liner 'Batavia,' both of which vessels subsequently united in taking off the 410 passengers. . . ."

THE ADVANTAGES CLAIMED BY THE USE OF THE ABOVE SYSTEM (intended to be called THE JOHNSON-VARLEY TUNING SYSTEM) are:—

(1) SECRECY. (The impossibility of messages being tapped.)
(2) NON-INTERFERENCE of one message with another. This embodies the following :—
    (A) Immediate receipt of messages.
    (B) Saving of time and electrical power as repetition of messages is avoided.
    (C) Prevention of the frequent irrevocable loss of distress or other urgent messages.
    (D) Absence of necessity of separating stations by distance.
    (E) Impossibility of the messages being drowned or confused by rival systems, or enemies in warfare or manœuvres.

(3) **INTERCOMMUNICATION** (a) to a required limited extent, say, between all the ships or stations of one Squadron or Company; or (b) to an unlimited extent by a "common" tune, for distress signals, weather reports, or any news of a general character.

(4) **TRIPLE RECEIVERS** (of 3 tunes for the simultaneous reception of secret, semi-secret, and general messages.

(5) **CHEAPNESS AND SIMPLICITY** of apparatus.

(6) **ELIMINATION OF DANGER** to operators.

Each one of these six advantages is of immense importance.

The Directors propose to demonstrate in a public and practical way the Johnson-Varley Tuning System, giving the Admiralty, the Post Office, and important Wireless Telegraph Companies the opportunity of attending and attempting by any means to tap the secret messages or to destroy or interfere with them in any way, and they are confident that as a result of these demonstrations important contracts will be entered into, and licenses granted, which will assure the formation of a Company to commercially exploit the system, and that the whole interest of this Syndicate will be taken over at the purchase price (payable partly in cash and partly in Shares) of £150,000 as suggested in the Syndicate's original prospectus, which after paying expenses will be distributed among the Shareholders of the Syndicate.

To provide the necessary funds for this the balance of the Share Capital—viz., 2,479 Shares of £1 each—is now offered at par. These Shares should be highly remunerative in a very short time.

Copies of two recent reports by Messrs. Johnson and Varley, relating to the Johnson-Varley Tuning System, are given below:—

"82, NEWINGTON GREEN ROAD, ISLINGTON, N.,
March 27th, 1909.

To the Chairman and Directors of
THE JOHNSON SECRET WIRELESS TELEGRAPH AND TELEPHONE TESTING SYNDICATE LIMITED.

GENTLEMEN,

From September, 1908, I have been working in conjunction with Mr. A. T. M. Johnson in testing and determining the best means to produce effective "Secret Wireless Telegraphy," and we have so far succeeded in proving the capability of working a combined system for transmitting and receiving definitely tuned signals, that we were enabled to put before you a programme of tests, and demonstrate each item by actual experiment, and I am fully convinced that a most valuable property can be realised from the invention.

The Transmitting Apparatus having a tunable adjustment system, can be regulated for various periodicities of signalling and thereby brought into unison with the Johnson tell-tale reed and relay receiving reeds when the latter responds in syntonic synchronism with the periodicity of the transmitted electric waves. It is this sympathetic sensitiveness of adjustment between the receiving relays and the transmitted electric waves which ensures an absolute secret system of Wireless Telegraphy.

I am, Gentlemen, yours very truly,
(*Signed*) FREDERICK H. VARLEY, M.I.E.E., F.R.A.S.

I fully endorse Mr. F. H. Varley's statements in this Report.

(*Signed*) A. T. M. JOHNSON, A.M.M.C.I.E."

"CARLTON HOUSE, 77, SHEPHERDS BUSH ROAD, WEST KENSINGTON PARK, LONDON, W.,
March 27th, 1909.

To the Chairman and Directors of
THE JOHNSON SECRET WIRELESS TELEGRAPH AND TELEPHONE TESTING SYNDICATE LIMITED.

GENTLEMEN,

Since September 1st, 1908, Mr. Frederick Henry Varley and myself have been actively engaged in formulating a combined system for working Mr. Varley's newly invented Make and Break with my Secret Wireless Telegraphic and Telephonic Apparatus, and I am pleased to say that the trifling obstacles with which we were confronted at the commencement of our labours have been successfully overcome, and we can now confidently assure you that the combined method works admirably, as evidenced by yourselves at the demonstration conducted in your presence at the residence of Dr. Richardson, 41, Brook Street, Grosvenor Square, on Tuesday, the 23rd inst., and which was as follows:—

ITEM 1.

An exposition of the **new** method of **Secret** Wireless Telegraphy and Telephony by differentiation, by which system alone a Secret Message can be sent and received.

ITEM 2.

To demonstrate the action of the Differentiator in the transmission of a **Secret Wireless Message** by means of a Morse Key.

ITEM 3.

To prove the receipt of an **absolutely Secret Wireless Message**.

ITEM 4.

To prove the impossibility of tapping, interrupting, or in any way interfering with messages transmitted by the Johnson-Varley System, by the use of two Telephonic Receivers employed simultaneously.

ITEM 5.

To demonstrate the receipt of a Secret Message by a syntonised Sounder.

ITEM 6.

To prove the possibility of receiving a positively **Secret** Message by a syntonised Tape Recording Instrument.

Accordingly, if the necessary appliances, as per Schedule annexed to Mr. Varley's Report, be supplied, Mr. Varley and myself are prepared to undertake the successful transmission and reception of Secret Wireless messages, to and from any distance, without fear of the messages being tapped, interrupted or in any way interfered with by any other system, any distance you may desire, provided the requisite current and coils, with sufficient carrying capacity be obtained, and suitably situated and equipped Wireless Stations be secured, approximately within eight weeks from the date that we receive definite instructions to give the orders for the necessary apparatus.

Yours faithfully,
(*Signed*) A. T. M. JOHNSON, A.M.M.C.I.E.

I fully endorse Mr. A. T. M. Johnson's statements in this Report.
(*Signed*) FREDERICK H. VARLEY, M.I.E.E., F.R.A.S."

The Syndicate reserves to itself the right to pay a commission of 5 per cent. to any person procuring or agreeing to procure subscriptions for all or any of the Shares now offered.

A brokerage of 3d. per Share will be paid on all Shares allotted in respect of applications bearing Brokers' Stamps.

Applications for Shares should be made on the Form accompanying this Prospectus, and should be sent to the Syndicate's Bankers, at the address stated on the Form, together with a remittance for the amount due upon application.

Where no allotment is made the deposit will be returned in full, and where the number of Shares allotted is less than the number applied for the balance of the deposit will be applied towards the remaining payments.

Interest at the rate of Five per cent. per annum will be chargeable upon payments in arrear.

Failure to pay any further instalments when due will render previous payments liable to forfeiture.

Prospectuses and Forms of Application can be obtained from the Syndicate's Bankers, Auditors, Solicitors, or from the Syndicate's Offices.

Copies of the Syndicate's Memorandum and Articles of Association and of the above-mentioned Contracts (or copies thereof), can be inspected at the Offices of the Solicitors to the Syndicate at any time during the usual business hours.

LONDON, *August 5th*, 1909.

APPENDIX 9

Letter addressed by Marconi Wireless Telegraph Co. Ltd. to its Shareholders, 1909

(Courtesy David Evans)

MARCONI'S WIRELESS TELEGRAPH COMPANY
LIMITED.

WATERGATE HOUSE,
YORK BUILDINGS,
ADELPHI, LONDON, W.C.,
12th October, 1909.

DEAR SIR (OR MADAM),

I am instructed by my Directors to send you the following information in connection with the agreement recently concluded between The Marconi International Marine Communication Company, Limited, this Company and the Postmaster-General.

The agreement provides, in consideration of the payment of £15,000 to the Companies, for the transfer to the Post Office of the Coast Stations in the United Kingdom owned by the International Company, and for the surrender of the rights which the International Company enjoyed under its agreement of August, 1904, with the Post Office for licenses or facilities in respect of these Coast Stations. Marconi's Wireless Telegraph Company is interested in this matter principally as a Shareholder.

The Post Office also secures the right of using, free of further payment, the existing Marconi Patents and any future patents or improvements, for the term of fourteen years, but under the following conditions as set forth in Clause 3 of the agreement :—

The use of the inventions provided for by this clause shall extend to :—

(1) All communications for all purposes between stations of the Postmaster-General in the United Kingdom on the one hand, and ships at sea on the other hand ; and

(2) All communications for all purposes between stations of the Postmaster-General in Great Britain or Ireland on the one hand, and stations on the Isle of Man, the Channel Islands, or any other outlying island on the other hand, and between any two stations on the said Isle of Man, the Channel Islands or any other outlying island ; and

(3) All communications for all purposes between a Post Office cable ship on the one hand, and any wireless telegraph station on shore or on a ship on the other hand ; and

(4) All communications for any purpose except the transmission of inland written telegrams accepted from the public between any two stations of the Postmaster General.

Provided always that if the Postmaster General desires to use the said inventions for the transmission of inland written telegrams accepted from the public between any station in the United Kingdom and any other station in the United Kingdom (other than stations in the Isle of Man, the Channel Islands and the other outlying British islands), or for any communication between any station in the United Kingdom and any station in a British possession or any foreign country, such use shall be on such terms as may be agreed on or settled in accordance with the provisions of section 29 of the Patents and Designs Act 1907.

Provided also that the Postmaster-General shall not use the said invention for the installation of wireless telegraphy on board any ship other than a Post Office cable ship or in any lighthouse or on any lightship except on the terms specified in section 29 of the Patents and Designs Act 1907.

This agreement also provides for the cancellation of all agreements between the Marconi Companies and Lloyd's, and thus has the beneficial result of putting an end to the litigation with Lloyd's which has continually existed, and caused great expenditure of time and money.

None of the stations belonging to Marconi's Wireless Telegraph Company, Limited, are included in the agreement with the Post Office. Moreover, the agreement does not affect the transatlantic stations at Poldhu and Clifden, nor does it in any way relate to the trans-oceanic business of Marconi's Wireless Telegraph Company, Limited.

My Directors are of the opinion that this agreement, whereby a very small portion of the business of the International Company has been transferred to the Post Office, is distinctly satisfactory to both Companies. The manufacturing business of Marconi's Wireless Telegraph Company will be affected beneficially, and the closer relations which are now established with His Majesty's Post Office will assist both the Companies in many ways, not only in this Country but also in the Colonies.

The foregoing explanation has been put forth at some length in consequence of the fact that it has been brought to the notice of the Directors that many Shareholders have misunderstood the scope of the agreement.

The Directors take this opportunity of referring to the fire, which, as the Shareholders will have learned from the Press, burnt down a considerable portion of the Canadian Company's transatlantic station at Glace Bay on the eve of its completion. Fortunately the damage was covered by insurance. Steps were immediately taken to reinstate the station, and Mr. Marconi, who is now at Glace Bay, reports that there is every reason to believe the Transatlantic Service will be re-opened early in the New Year.

I am, Dear Sir (or Madam),

Yours faithfully,

HENRY W. ALLEN,
Secretary.

List of Awards for Gallantry to Marconi Radio Officers during World War II

(Courtesy Marconi plc)

LIST OF AWARDS TO MARCONI RADIO OFFICERS FOR GALLANTRY AT SEA

as

announced in the *London Gazette* and *Lloyd's List*.

D.S.C.

Ambler, E. H.	Mason, C. P.	Walker, H. (R.N.V.R.)

GEORGE MEDAL

Dennis, D. W.

M.B.E.

*Andrews, F. G.	*Garstin, G. K.	*Marshall, C. S.
Arthurs, A. M.	Glen, G. R.	Murphy, E.
*Bacon, N. J.	Glendinning, J.	*Norcliffe, H. W. H.
Campbell, E.	Golden, D. H.	Palmer, C.
Cardwell, W. S.	*Hackston, G. W.	Parkinson, W.
Carlyle, T.	Hackworthy, W. H.	Powell, S.
*Coleman, C. A.	*Haines, S. D.	Richardson, G.
*Coleman, N. M.	Hodgson, E.	Riordan, P. A.
Cummins, P. J.	Horn, H. S.	*Simkins, T.
Dowling, R. J.	Hosking, L. G.	*Smith, B. H.
Edwards, D.	Huey, A.	Taylor, S. J.
Evans, J. R.	Jenkins, T. M.	Thompson, J. J.
Franklin, A. J.	King, B.	Walker, G.
Fryer, G. K.		

* Indicates that the recipient was also awarded Lloyd's War Medal for bravery at sea.

COMMENDATIONS

Abbott, J. M.	Currie, R. W.	Harvey, V. S.
Adamson, G.	Darton, M. H.	Haworth, H.
Archer, G. J. M.	Darwin, P. J.	Hill, L. D.
Baker, T. J. F.	Davies, J. I.	Hindle, G. M.
*Barrett, M. W. K.	Dempster, J. D.	Hodgson, C. W.
Barrett, R. F.	Dennis, A.	Hodgson, E.
Bentley, E. M.	Everett, W. J.	(Also awarded M.B.E.
Bradshaw, E. H.	Franks, P. A.	previously)
Broomfield, H. F. C.	Gilpin, J. G.	Hughes, R. W.
Brown, W. M. A.	Graham, W. R.	John, R. P. D.
Child, E. C.	Hale, F. J.	Kemp, J. E.
Clarke, J. W.	Hardy, G. R. V.	Livingstone, A. M.
Cockburn, T.	Harrison, W.	Lovie, J.

COMMENDATIONS

Low, C. S.	Rogers, H. J.	*Clark, F. R.
Lyons, D. I.	Saunders, J. E.	*Duncan, E. H.
Major, E.	Sharman, J. O.	Hare, J. E.
Martin, T. H.	Thompson, D. H.	*Hay, J. W. E.
Martinson, N. C.	Thompson, J. E.	*Magee, J. H. A.
Moore, J.	Townsend, J. A. E.	Murphy, M. J.
Murphy, J.	Trewren, N. L.	Newbold, R. A.
Murray, W. G.	Walsh, C.	*O'Keefe, C. G.
McDonald, T.	Watson, E.	Oldfield, W. F.
McGregor, J.	Whiting, W. Y.	Reilly, W.
O'Hanlon, M. S. A.	Worrall, K. J. D.	Shepherd, J.
O'Keeffe, P. J.	Zeitlyn, O. D.	Smith, A. A. E.
Owen, E. A.		*Stewart, R.
Parcell, S.	*Posthumous*	*Sturdy, E.
Perrin, A.	Alexander, T. F.	Taylor, J.
Proctor, R. L.	*Barker, G. T.	Ward, G. W.
Raeburn, G. A.	Bowden, J. N.	*Watson, J. V.
Richmond, P. V.	Butterworth, A. R. C.	*Wilson, J. F.
Roberts, K. J.	Cannell, B. I.	Williamson, A. L.
Robinson, K. W.	Carpenter, S. G.	Williamson, H.

LLOYD'S WAR MEDAL FOR BRAVERY AT SEA

Andrews, F. G.	Marshall, C. S.	*Posthumous*
Bacon, N. J.	Norcliffe, H. W. H.	Hay, J. W. E.
Barrett, M. W. K.	Simkins, T.	Magee, J. H.
Coleman, C. A.	Smith, B. H.	O'Keefe, C. G.
Coleman, N. M.		Stewart, R.
Dennis, D. W.	*Posthumous*	Sturdy, E.
Garstin, G. K.	Barker, G. T.	Watson, J. V.
Hackston, G. W.	Clark, F. R.	Wilson, J. F.
Haines, S. D.	Duncan, E. B.	

SILVER MEDAL OF ROYAL HUMANE SOCIETY

Fairley, D. S. (Also awarded Stanhope Gold Medal for 1941 given by the
 Royal Humane Society for bravest deed of the year)
Pye, L. C.

MENTIONED IN DESPATCHES

Moody, J. T. W.	Newcombe, A. A.	Walker, H. (twice). (R.N.V.R.)

BRONZE MEDAL FOR SAVING LIFE AT SEA

Loughlin, C. M.	Thayne, A. C.

APPENDIX 11

Typical Wireless Cabins over the Years

117. An early wireless cabin, c.1900.
(Photograph: Marconi plc)

118. Marconi's wireless cabin on the *Tongue* lightship
(same equipment as on the *East Goodwin* lightship).
(Photograph: Marconi plc)

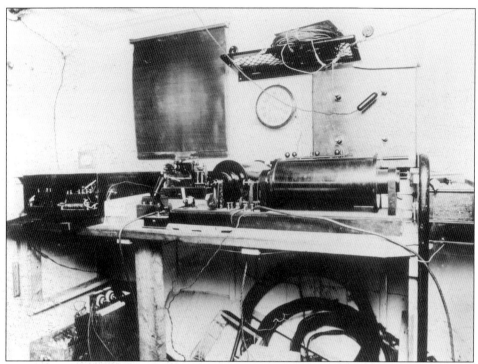

119. Wireless room on the S.S. *Philadelphia*, 1902.
(Photograph: Marconi plc)

120. Wireless room on the R.M.S. *Olympic.*
(Photograph: Marconi plc)

121. An early ship's wireless installation, 1½ kilowatt rotating spark gap and induction coil emergency transmitter, and Multiple Tuner with Magnetic detector for reception.
(Photograph: Marconi plc)

122. Marconi cabin on R.M.S. *Lusitania.*
(Photograph: Marconi plc)

123. A ship's wireless cabin, circa late 20s.
(Photograph: Marconi plc)

124. A ship's wireless cabin, circa early 30s.
(Photograph: Marconi plc)

125. A typical liner wireless cabin, circa mid 60s.
(Photograph: Marconi plc)

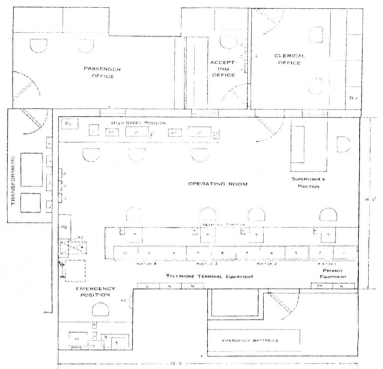

Layout of operating room and associated offices on R.M.S. 'Queen Mary.'

Operating Position.
(T) Typewriter well.
(K) Key.

High Speed Position.
(P) Perforator.
(AT) High-speed key.
(U) Undulator.
(RU) Rectifier unit.
(K) Key.

Emergency Position.
(M) Transmitter.
(R) Receiver.
(L) Auto alarm key.
(K) Key.
(B) Charging board.
(CB) Battery control board.

General.
(J) Junction boxes.
(C) Clocks (G.M.T.—Ship—N.Y.).
(V) Singing suppressor equipment.
(VU) Singing suppressor mains unit.
(N) Delay networks.
(PE) Privacy equipment.
(PB) Power board.
(AC) Aerial connector box.
(NC) Night counter.
(A) Aerial lead-in.
(EL) Escape ladder.
(BR) High-fidelity broadcast receiver.

126. Part of the radio operating room on board *Queen Mary*. On the right, the main operating positions; on the left, the high-speed telegraphy and supervisor's positions.

(Photograph: Radio Bygones)

127. A corner of the Radio Control Room, R.M.S. *Queen Mary.*
(Photograph: Sydney Shacklock)

128. Redifon SSB Receiver on *Queen Elizabeth*, 1958.
(Photograph: Brian Richards)

List of Further Reading

A History of the Marconi Company. W. J. Baker, 1970.

A Pinch of Salt. John Agnew and John Russell (Pub. JAR Partnership, 21 Landcross Drive, Abingdon Vale, Northampton, NN3 3LR).

Forgotten Empress. David Zeni, 2001.

Deep-Sea 'Sparks'. Olive J. Carroll, 1993 (Canadian).

Marconi and his Wireless Stations in Wales. Hari Williams, 1999.

Marconi at the Lizard. Courtney Rowe, 2000. Published by the Trevithic Society, Lizard, Cornwall.

Marconi's Atlantic Leap. Gordon Bussey, 2000.

Marconi My Beloved. Maria Cristina Marconi, 1999.

My Father, Marconi. Degna Marconi, 1996.

One Hundred Years of Marine Radio. W. D. Goodwin, 1995.

New Zealand by Sea. John Russell, 2000. JAR Partnership, 21 Landcross Drive, Abingdon Vale, Northampton, NN3 3LR.

Sparks at Sea. R. W. Chandler, 1973.

Sparks on the Bridge. Harry Hutson, Cleethorpes.

The Fourth Service. John Slader, 1995.

Titanic. Peter Boyd-Smith, 1998. Published by Steamship Publications, 78 Northam Road, Southampton, SO14 0PB.

Titanic Disaster HEARINGS. Tom Kuntz, 1998. Published by Pocket Books, New York.

Watchers of the Waves. B. Faulkner, 1996.

Wireless at Sea. H. E. Hancock, 1950.

RELEVANT SOCIETIES & ORGANISATIONS

RADIO OFFICER'S ASSOCIATION – Hon. Membership Secretary, John Russell, 21, Landcross Drive, Abingdon Vale, Northampton, NN3 3LR.

RADIO SOCIETY OF GREAT BRITAIN – Lambda House, Cranborne Road, Potters Bar, Herts., EN6 3JE.

THE RADIO AMATEUR OLD TIMERS' ASSOCIATION – Hon. Secretary, Mrs Sheila Gabriel, Millbrook House, 3 Mill Drove, Bourne, Lincs., PE10 9BX.

THE BRITISH VINTAGE WIRELESS SOCIETY – Membership Secretary: Mike Barker, 59 Dunsford Close, Hillside Park, Swindon, Wilts., SN1 4PW.

RELEVANT PERIODICALS

Sea Breezes. Editor: Captain A. C. Douglas, Units 28-30, Spring Valley Industrial Estate, Braddan, Isle of Man, IM2 2QS.

Shipping Today & Yesterday. Editor: John M. Young, Subscriptions, HPC Publishing, Drury Lane, St Leonards On Sea, East Sussex, TN38 9BJ.

Practical Wireless. Arrowsmith Court, Station Approach, Broadstone, Dorset, BH18 8PW.

Radio Bygones. Editor: Mike Kenward, Wimborne Publishing Ltd., 408 Wimborne Road East, Ferndown, Dorset, BH22 9ND.

Acknowledgements

THE NUMBER OF PEOPLE who have helped in the course of my researches for this book forms a very long list, and it is difficult to decide how to keep it within reasonable bounds. Researching the book proved for me to be an extraordinary experience; for it was as if I had opened and entered through a door of forty years ago. As well as reviving old memories and experiences, it brought me once again into contact with many old friends and colleagues whom I had never expected to see again. A change of name, which took place twenty years ago, seemed to fade into insignificance, and my life has been enriched and illuminated as a consequence.

A long list of names, unsupported by details, seems to me not the best way to deal with it, and I have opted instead to specifically mention those whose contributions appear in the book, and without whose help it literally could have not been brought to a successful conclusion. I hope that everybody else will accept my sincere and heartfelt thanks, and my assurance that its aim is (adding to other excellent works already published) to record the contribution made by Radio Officers to the Merchant Navy and the Nation and in three wars.

LOUISE WEYMOUTH – Company Archivist, Marconi PLC, ably supported by her Assistant, Pam Betts, has been throughout a miracle of laid-back efficiency. As its name implies, the book is not intended to be a history of the Marconi Company, but the fact remains that the history of wireless at sea is synonymous at least for the first twenty years with the history of Guglielmo Marconi and his company. And I have chosen to present him as the first Radio Officer at sea. The book could not have been produced in its present form without the help of Marconi PLC and Louise Weymouth.

DAVID EVANS – the last proprietor of the British School of Telegraphy, for information about the history of the school and much other fascinating ephemera relating to the history of wireless at sea.

Mr E. A. DREWERY – whose life has encapsulated the history of wireless communication on deep-sea trawlers, without whose help the very important chapter on deep-sea trawlers could never have been adequately dealt with.

HARRY HUTSON – whose book *Sparks on the Bridge* is essential reading for anyone interested in deep-sea trawlers, and who has allowed me to make use of it.

GEORGE H. W. JOHNSON – Ex-Radio Officer and colleague, and currently Mayor of Colwyn Bay, North Wales, for much support and valuable material.

KEN KLOSSOR – late of the Radio and Electronic Officers Union, who has given me much invaluable help and support.

PROFESSOR BRIAN N. COTTON, F.I.E.E., Chairman of the Radio Officers Association.

JOHN RUSSELL – Hon. Membership Secretary, Radio Officers Association.

BERNARD HAZLETON – Secretary of the Marconi Veterans Association.

Mrs GAYNOR WEBBER – who made available a photograph of her uncle, Donald Lamont, of the *Trevessa*.

KENNETH PIZEY – who provided much rare and valuable material.

BRIAN RICHARDS – of late in charge of Government Ship Wireless Inspections, for information regarding the Regulations for Carrying Radio Officers, and much other help.

PETER BOYD-SMITH – of Steamship Publications, Southampton, for particular advice and help.

DALLAS BRADSHAW, ALICE MOLLISON (Mrs Alice Cathro) and CAROLE LANGLEY – who blazed the trail for female Radio Officers in the British Merchant Navy, and provided me with details of their training and careers.

PETER BARBER – torpedoed while serving as a Radio Officer on the *Clan MacWhirter* in August 1941, who provided me with details and photographs. Sadly, Mr Barber died before this book could be published.

MAURICE GLOVER – Chief Radio Officer of the *Elmdale*, attacked by a Japanese submarine off Colombo in 1941 and later torpedoed by a German submarine. For details and photographs.

COURTNEY ROWE – of Church Cove, Lizard, and the Lizard Women's Institute, for valuable information and photographs.

SYDNEY SHACKLOCK – Chief Radio Officer of the *Auckland Star*, torpedoed in 1940 on a return voyage from Australia to the UK , and again in 1944, while serving on the *Empire Tourist*, when homeward bound from Archangel in an Arctic convoy. For details and photographs.

PATRICK WATSON – who provided me with details and photographs relating to the experience and life of his uncle, Radio Officer Alfred Pink, who was present at the battle of Coronel, Chile, in November 1914.

In addition to the foregoing, I wish to record my thanks to Jenny Sabine and Dr Keith Greenlaw for reading the proofs of the book, and once again to all those concerned in its production at Dinefwr Press. This is the fourth book they have produced for me, and I cannot speak too highly of their high standards, professional skill, and ability to deliver on time. Their contribution went beyond printing, for it included editing at the highest level, and the creation of the front and back covers.

Finally, I must say that any errors are my responsibility. This book is bound to enter the field of vision of many ex-Radio Officers and other experts, and it is likely that many will regret the omission of items of particular importance to them. But in selecting from the large amount of material available, for instance the numerous training colleges, and multiplicity of examples of Radio Officer's heroism, I considered there was a danger of duplication which would be undesirable, quite apart from limitations of space.

In the course of researching this book, I have been surprised at the amount of interest the subject has aroused, and not just among ex-Radio Officers. And for that reason I have tried to make it as readable as possible to a much wider public.

I will be glad to hear from anyone interested in the subject; and my address and telephone number will be found at the beginning of the book.

Index